HANNAH
SAVES THE
WORLD 2

a.m. luzzader

HANNAH SAVES THE WORLD

BOOK 2: MIDDLE GRADE MYSTERY FICTION

A.M. LUZZADER

ILLUSTRATED BY
CHADD VANZANTEN

KNOWLEDGE FOREST
PRESS

Published by Knowledge Forest Press
P.O. Box 6331
Logan, UT 84341

Ebook ISBN-13: 978-1-949078-26-8
Paperback ISBN-13: 978-1-949078-25-1
Hardback ISBN-13: 979-8722473-71-4

Cover design by Sleepy Fox Studio

Developmental and Copy Editing by Chadd VanZanten

Interior illustrations by Chadd VanZanten

To Juniper
Lover of kitties and girl with bright eyes

IN A HOUSE on Shady Lane in the pleasant town of Cardwick, George Gevol awoke early one morning to find a hulking robot standing motionless at the foot of his bed.

George didn't have his glasses on, and he wasn't fully awake. Also, the sun had not risen yet, and the blinds on the windows were drawn shut. And so George had to squint his eyes to see, but, yes, there was definitely a rather large robot in his room. The robot had eyes that blazed cold and eerily purple, and it stood over six feet tall. Even in the low light, he could see that it was powerfully built, with impressively large robotic pistons for muscles. George knew that this mechanical beast could easily pull down George's entire house, wall by wall, without having to try very hard. It loomed over the gloomy room, which made George feel quite puny.

George fumbled around on his nightstand and retrieved a pair of eyeglasses with round, wire-rimmed frames. He put them on, smiled sleepily at the robot, and said, "Ah, good morning, Robert. How are you today?"

"I am functioning within established parameters," said Robert the Robot, which was his way of saying, "I am doing just fine, thank you."

"Splendid," said George.

"I trust you slept well?" the robot asked George. "It is your big day today."

"Yes, Robert," replied George, throwing back the blankets and rising from his bed. George was a lanky man with a head of wild, white hair and a bristly beard to match. "I slept splendidly!"

"That is good," said Robert, his robotic voice sounding pleased.

"You know, Robert," said George, "it's a big day for you, too. Are you ready?"

"Affirmative," replied Robert, bowing slightly again.

"Splendid, splendid," said George.

"Shall we proceed to the kitchen?" asked Robert,

gesturing toward the bedroom door. "It is my turn to make breakfast."

"Yes!" George followed the robot toward the kitchen. "Robert, I'd like a bountiful breakfast. I think I could eat about two dozen eggs, three pounds of bacon, and a stack of buttered toast two feet tall!"

Robert stopped and turned to George. "That may be a problem, George," said Robert. "We have only ten eggs in the refrigeration unit, and there is only one half of a loaf of bread in the bread box, which will measure only eighty-five millimeters in height when toasted and stacked on a plate. Our bacon stockpile is likewise insufficient to fulfill your request. Shall I arrange to acquire additional breakfast supplies?"

George chuckled and patted Robert on his back. This felt a little like patting a truck on its fender. "No, no, Robert. That won't be necessary. You see, I was exaggerating. Or, you might say I was *eggs*-agerating. Remember? We sometimes exaggerate or say silly things for the sake of—"

"—humor," said Robert. "Of course."

"Yes," said George. "I was just *kidding*."

"Yes," said Robert, nodding. "No human would actually consume such quantities of food. It would have many unpleasant side-effects. I see now. A joke. *Kidding*."

"Splendid," said George. "You're learning!"

"Yes," said Robert. "I did not understand at first because the quality of the humor was not very high."

George chuckled sheepishly and shrugged. "You're probably right. I'll try harder next time."

"Thank you."

George Gevol was a scientist and inventor. He had moved to Cardwick only a few years before, relocating his entire laboratory and fabrication facility to take advantage of certain tax incentives, but also to get away from the bustle and boom of the big city. George was fond of Cardwick, with its trimmed grass, tidy homes, and rows of shade trees.

There had been a recent rash of U.F.O. reports in Cardwick, which was odd, but George nevertheless found the little town reserved, restful, and refreshing.

George's specialty was robots. He had spent years researching robotics and artificial intelligence. He had invented many kinds of robots and robotic devices. One of them was a robotic chair that followed you around until you were ready to sit down. He'd also invented a robotic dishwasher that waited patiently next to the dinner table until everyone was finished eating, whereupon it collected the dishes into itself for washing.

As you might have already guessed, George also invented and built Robert the Robot. Robert could do many things humans could do. Robert helped George with research, manufacturing, and house-work, but George and Robert were also friends. They watched TV and even played catch with a football in the backyard. Robert had a very advanced computer network for a brain. George called it a "neural network," and he'd taught Robert's brain many things, including the rules of chess, how to play piano, and various ways to make breakfast.

"Putting the jokes aside," said Robert as they reached the kitchen, "how many eggs would you like for breakfast?"

George laughed and said, "Oh, I think two eggs will be *eggs*-cellent, Robert. Over-easy, please."

"Coming right up," said Robert. He put on his apron and opened the refrigerator.

As the robot collected pans and spatulas and food, George sat at the kitchen table, looking at the screen of his laptop computer for what must have been the fiftieth time in the past few days.

Today was the first day of George's vacation, and he was quadruple-checking the details of his flight and vacation schedule. The airline George had booked with was Astonishing Airlines, and they had a nasty habit of changing George's business flights at the last moment. He was concerned they might try to change his vacation flight.

But a grin spread over George's face as he clicked on his airline reservation and found that it was unchanged. His flight would take off that very evening, at 7 p.m., and the next day he'd be in Australia.

George was terribly excited. This was his first vacation in a long time. George loved working on his robots and research, but for ten years, he'd almost forgotten that vacations existed.

"It's finally here, Robert," said George looking up from his computer. "My vacation at last! You know, I was beginning to think this day would never arrive."

"I do not understand, George," said Robert, flipping the eggs with delightfully delicate dexterity. "Time passes quite predictably, does it not? Did you experience a problem with the space-time continuum?"

"Ah, Robert." George shook his head and laughed. "You always take things very literally, don't you? Let me explain. In certain situations, time *seems* to pass more slowly or more quickly—

depending on what you're waiting for. For example, if I'm waiting for something unpleasant, like having a tooth pulled, time may *seem* to pass by fast. If I'm waiting for my first vacation in ten years, time *seems* to creep by like a snail."

"That is very strange," said Robert, "because the passage of time is constant for everyone, unless of course you are traveling at rates that are close to the speed of light, and even then, the differences are relative."

"Yes," said George, grinning and nodding. "Technically, you're correct, as you usually are."

Robert brought the eggs and bacon and toast to the table.

"Well, this looks simply splendid, Robert! Thank you, my friend."

"You are most welcome, George," replied the robot. "And if you are worried about the condition of your human teeth, perhaps when you return from your trip, we can replace them with titanium tooth units like those you forged for me." Robert parted his robotic lips to reveal his gleaming, titanium teeth.

George chuckled. Even though Robert was a robot, and he got most of his energy from power outlets and solar panels, George had built Robert with a mouth and teeth and a stomach, so that he could consume human food. George and Robert ate all their meals together so that Robert could perhaps learn to appreciate things like chocolate cake, tacos, pizza, and fried eggs.

"No," said George. "My teeth are fine as far as I know. That was just an example."

Robert nodded and took a seat at the table across from George and they began to eat their breakfast, which, thanks to Robert, was perfectly prepared.

"Well, Robert," said George, "I'm sure you're going to be just fine while I'm gone, but do you have any last questions before I take off?"

Robert looked up from his eggs and bacon and said, "No, my neural network and memory banks are functioning normally. I have retained all of your instructions."

"Splendid," said George, popping a curl of bacon into his mouth. "Would you mind if I quiz you, then?"

"Not at all," said Robert. "Proceed."

"All right. What if there is an emergency? Like a fire?"

"If an unexpected incident arises that I am incapable of addressing by myself, I am to call the relevant civil authorities, such as the Cardwick Fire Department or Police Department. I am to transmit all necessary information to them, and then follow their recommendations."

"Excellent answer," said George. "And what about me? What if you need to contact me?"

"Because you will be in a wilderness region of the Australian Outback, none of your communication devices will function normally. And so if I must contact you, I should call or send a message to the travel bureau and notify them. They will then notify you, and you will in turn contact me at your earliest opportunity."

"Splendid, Robert." George gave Robert a thumbs-up. "And the houseplants?"

"I will monitor the growing material in their containers and regularly dispense carefully measured quantities of water so that their photosynthesis continues without interruption."

The scientist sighed with satisfaction. "I see my scrutiny was superfluous. You are evidently equipped for every eventuality."

"As I mentioned," said Robert, lifting his napkin from his lap, "your instructions and guidance are perfectly preserved in my neural network and memory banks." Robert dabbed at his mouth with the napkin, not because there was anything to wipe away, but because he had seen George do the same.

"Of course," replied George. "However, there is one piece of advice that I have been saving for this morning."

"Is that so?" asked Robert. "What is it?"

George smiled. Robert was certainly one of his finest inventions. When George had first built Robert, he was very satisfied with the robot's engineering, construction, and programming. But Robert had since taken on a life of his own, and now he was much more like a person than a machine.

George wanted to tell Robert that he shouldn't worry while he was on his own, and that he should try to relax, enjoy some time off from working in the lab, and try not to go to extremes. George wanted to tell Robert to read some books or watch some movies, and not work too hard. Robert was a friend and work partner to George, and for once George wanted to give his robotic companion some friendly advice, rather than just instructions.

And so George sat up straight and cleared his throat. "Robert, what I'm about to tell you is more important than watering the plants or taking care of the lab while I'm gone. It's the most important thing I have to tell you."

All of Robert's sensors were actively, attentively, anxiously listening for what George would say next.

But just then, George's phone rang.

George glanced at the phone and saw that Astonishing Airlines was calling. He raised one finger to signal Robert to wait while he took the call. Robert sat motionless in his chair, waiting.

George put the phone to his ear. "George Gevol here."

"Hi, Mr. Gevol," said the caller. "This is Anthony from Astonishing Airlines, and I have some bad news about your flight to Australia. Due to bad weather, your flight has been postponed for one week."

"Oh, no," groaned George, covering his face with his hand. "This is terrible. I'm scheduled to go on a month-long walkabout. If I don't get to Australia in time, the whole trip will be spoiled."

"I'm sorry, sir," said Anthony. "Air travel can be somewhat unpredictable."

George put his hand on his forehead and said, "Is there nothing to be done? I've been planning this trip for months."

He has been planning his vacation for 125 days, thought Robert.

"Hang on," said Anthony.

George heard the tapping of keys on a keyboard. This went on for several minutes.

"Mr. Gevol," said Anthony, "I can put you on another flight, but it's departing in only a few hours. You'd have to get here right away."

"I can do that!" cried George. "Just give me the details!"

"Okay, sir," said Anthony. "Have you got something to write with?"

George scrambled to his desk, knocking over his favorite potted hydrangea and scattering office supplies everywhere. Then he stooped over the desk, pencil in hand. However, just at that hour of the day, a beam of light from the rising sun shone brightly through a nearby accent window and glared directly into George's eyes. He tried turning this way and that at the desk, but the glare only worsened, reflecting and refracting off his eyeglasses.

"Yes," huffed George, "I have a pencil—" But the sun seemed determined to blind him. He squinted and blinked and couldn't see the desk or his paper. He held up a hand to block the sun, but then he couldn't write.

At last, George placed a hand over his phone and turned to Robert in desperation.

"Robert!" George implored. "Block out that infernal sun!"

Robert was swift and efficient. He went swiftly

to the accent window and drew the blinds closed. This took him 3.75 seconds, and when he'd completed the task, he saw that George was able to write down the needed information.

"Yes," said George, scribbling furiously. "Flight 8234. Yes! Okay. Splendid! Thank you, Anthony."

George ended the call, pocketed the paper, and turned to face his robot friend again. "Robert," he said, "as you might have noticed, there's been a big change of plans."

Robert nodded his robot head.

"Instead of taking off at 7 p.m. tonight, I'm leaving in just a couple of hours. I have to go! Now!"

"It is fortunate that you are already packed," said Robert. "I will help you with your luggage."

"Thank you, my friend," said George.

They worked quickly, with Robert working more quickly than George, of course, and soon George was ready to go. But before George got into his car, he held out his hand to Robert. They shook hands.

"Remember what I told you," said George, climbing into his car. "And I'll see you in a month or so."

"Splendid," said Robert.

George was very soon on an airliner headed to the Southern Hemisphere. It had been rush-rush-

rush and dash-dash-dash. George was frazzled and feeling faint. However, Anthony's plan had worked, and George's trip was back on schedule. He settled into his seat, grinned, and breathed a sigh of relief.

But then something occurred to George. He'd wanted to tell Robert to take it easy, to enjoy the vacation, and not be so serious and extreme all the time. But then the call had come from Astonishing Airlines and the rest of the morning was a chaotic blur. Had he told Robert what he wanted to say? He couldn't remember.

Perhaps I should call Robert, thought George. *Just to make sure.*

George took his phone from his pocket, but then he remembered that he couldn't call from the airplane. He was feeling quite nervous when suddenly he remembered his own advice.

Take it easy, George told himself. *Robert the Robot will be just fine.*

CHAPTER 2

Mia Miller was almost finished with her piano lesson when something in the corner of her eye grabbed her attention.

It was a face. To be specific, it was the face of Mia's best friend, Hannah.

As always, Hannah wore giant sunglasses and electric blue lipstick. Her hair was tinted light blue, but Mia knew that could change next week or tomorrow or even later that day.

Mia's hair was short and black and straight, and although she wore wire-framed eyeglasses, they were of a more ordinary size.

Under typical circumstances, Mia would have welcomed the sight of her best friend, but Hannah had a way of appearing out of nowhere, as if by magic, and the effect could be startling. Sometimes at school Mia would close her locker door and there was Hannah, who'd been standing silently behind it, and Mia would cry out, her books and notes flying everywhere. Or Mia would step out of the bathroom at home and there was Hannah, standing still and waiting, and Mia would spring back and almost slip into the shower stall.

Mia tried to remain focused on her piano lesson, but her fingers were already hitting the wrong notes. It sounded like a large cat was walking up and down the keys.

"Steady, Mia," said Mrs. Marjorie McMillan, Mia's piano teacher. "Start again, please, and slow down."

Mrs. McMillan didn't like it when her lessons were interrupted. Mia tried secretly signaling Hannah by tossing her head dismissively, trying to tell Hannah, "Get away from that window! Shoo!"

Hannah may have understood the signal, because her face quickly vanished. Mia was relieved and continued her scales.

But then Hannah's face appeared in another window, this one even closer to the piano. As usual, Hannah materialized suddenly and without warning, like a ghost in a scary movie. And this time she startled both Mrs. McMillan and Mia.

"Goodness!" cried Mrs. McMillan, clutching at the string of pearls she wore around her neck. "Who's that standing at your window?"

"That's just a silly friend of mine," said Mia with a nervous laugh, still frantically shooing Hannah away.

"You know I do not tolerate interruptions during lessons," said Mrs. McMillan sternly.

"Yes, ma'am," said Mia.

"Well," said Mrs. McMillan, her face softening into an approving smile, "in light of all the progress you've made, I'll overlook it this time. And there are only four minutes remaining in your lesson, so let's call it a day. But please tell your playmate to avoid interrupting us in the future."

"Yes, ma'am," Mia repeated.

Mia walked Mrs. McMillan to the door, said goodbye, and then returned to the piano to put away her sheet music and workbook. When Mia turned around, Hannah was there, mere inches behind her. Mia was so startled, she fell back and made a tremendous cacophony on the piano keys.

"Hannah!" hissed Mia. "Why do you *do* that?"

"Do what?" replied Hannah.

"You have a way of suddenly appearing out of nowhere! It startles the beans out of me!"

"Hey," said Hannah with a shrug, "it's not my fault if your powers of perception aren't as piercing as mine."

"I guess," said Mia. "But please don't interrupt my piano lessons."

"Very well," said Hannah. "I wouldn't ordinarily intrude that way, but I've got something urgent to discuss with you."

"With you," said Mia, "it's *always* urgent."

"Indeed," replied Hannah. "I try to limit my focus to matters of great importance. In any case, do you remember when we solved the Mystery of the Playground Vandalism and the Secret Stockpile of Halloween Jumbo Ga-Ga Gooey Bars?"

"*That's* the official name of the case?" asked Mia, blinking in disbelief.

"Quite a mouthful, isn't it?" replied Hannah with an embarrassed half-smile. "But anyway, do you remember when we were working that case, and you told me that we could all 'save the world' by doing good deeds no matter where we are? Like here in our own little town?"

"Sure, I remember," said Mia. She said this with a degree of caution, however, because she had a feeling Hannah might be leading up to another wild caper.

"Well, first, that was a great bit of advice," said Hannah.

Mia grinned and shrugged.

"Secondly," said Hannah, "as you may have guessed, I've found another case to save the world here in Cardwick. Step this way, please."

They went out onto Mia's porch and there they met Lacy Lambert, a girl from the neighborhood of their same age. Lacy was sitting glumly on the front stairs, but she stood up when Mia and Hannah came out onto the porch.

"Mia, I'm sure you know Lacy," said Hannah, gesturing at Lacy with an upturned hand.

"Yeah," said Mia. "Hi, Lacy. What's up? Are we all going to the park to play on the new swings? I've heard they're very nice. Or would you rather go inside and play a rousing round of Candyville?"

"Mia," Hannah huffed heavily, "I just told you we've got a new case to work on!"

"Right," said Mia with a sigh. "For a moment I thought maybe I'd misheard you, and today might be an ordinary day."

"No," said Hannah, slowly shaking her head, "with me around, you'll never have to worry about having an ordinary day."

"Yes," replied Mia in a sarcastic tone that Hannah failed to notice. "Lucky me."

"Lacy," said Hannah, "why don't you tell us your situation first, and then I'll make a few remarks afterwards."

"Okay," said Lacy. Her eyes were sad and downcast. "It's my cat, Mr. Meowgi. He ran away. He got out of the house and disappeared. We thought he'd come back when he got hungry, but he never did. We're all so worried about him."

Hannah stood with arms crossed, nodding gravely.

Mia had been hoping for a less-dramatic day—she really would have liked to go play on the swings. However, Mia also loved cats, and so she was sad to hear that Lacy's cat was missing.

"How long ago did Mr. Meowgi run away?" Mia asked Lacy.

"This past Wednesday," said Lacy. Small tears appeared in her eyes, but they didn't fall.

"Today's Saturday," said Mia, touching her chin. "So, that's four days ago."

Lacy nodded.

"I'm very sorry, Lacy," said Mia. "Have you searched the neighborhood?"

As Mia asked her questions and Lacy answered, Hannah looked from Mia to Lacy and back again.

"Yes," whimpered Lacy, and now the tears spilled from her eyes. "We searched the town and called the Animal Control Department. We put up posters. We even asked the Cardwick Police to be on the lookout for him. But he's still missing!" She sniffled and wiped her eyes.

Mia felt sorry for Lacy. Mia's family cat, Cindy Crawfurred, had once run away, too. She had eventually come home again, but for two whole weeks Mia's entire family thought they'd never see Cindy Crawfurred again.

"Well," said Mia, turning to Hannah, "I'd love to help out with this case. I was kinda hoping to just, you know, play on the swings at the park or watch cartoons, but we should help Lacy look for her little runaway kitty."

"He's not little," Lacy corrected. "He weighs twenty pounds and he's this big." She held out her hands to indicate the cat's size. Unless Lacy was exaggerating, Mr. Meowgi was quite a bit larger than a regulation basketball but somewhat smaller than a microwave oven.

"Gadzooks," said Mia, "this is a mighty big kitten. Should we get our bikes and start the search?"

"No," said Hannah.

Mia and Lacy both turned their heads to look at Hannah.

"No?" asked Mia, furrowing her brow. "But I thought we were taking this case?"

"Oh, we're taking the case all right," said Hannah, "but we won't be organizing any search parties. And I'll tell you why."

Lacy and Mia blinked at Hannah, waiting for her to continue.

Hannah stood on the porch with her arms still crossed over her chest. Also, one of her eyebrows was raised in a clever way, which she always did when she had something clever to say.

But she stayed quiet. This was one of Hannah's trademarks. She was waiting for the drama to deepen. She was amplifying the anticipation. Mia and Lacy seemed to lean forward now, waiting.

When the tension had risen to a pleasingly unpleasant level, Hannah took a breath and said, "We won't be searching for Mr. Meowgi because Mr. Meowgi did *not* run away from home!"

CHAPTER 3

IMMEDIATELY AFTER GEORGE GEVOL had zoomed off in the direction of the airport, Robert the Robot closed every window blind in the house and drew shut every curtain. Now he was also blocking every window with blankets and cardboard and duct tape.

If you are a robot, you'll understand why Robert was doing this. If you're not a robot (and you probably aren't), keep reading.

For all you human readers, an explanation about Robert's odd behavior is in order.

Let's rewind to the morning George left in a hurry to catch his rescheduled flight to Australia. You'll remember that George had something important to tell Robert. George was going to tell Robert that he shouldn't worry while he was on his own, and that he should relax, enjoy some time off, and avoid going to extremes. George was going to tell Robert to read some books, watch movies, and not take things so seriously.

But he never did.

Instead, George only *began* to say those things. He said, "Robert, what I'm about to tell you is more important than watering the plants or taking care of the lab while I'm gone. It's the most important thing I have to tell you."

Then he was interrupted.

If you'll recall, there came the fateful phone call from Anthony at Astonishing Airlines. And during the frantic fumbling for a pencil, writing down the information from Astonishing Airlines, and dealing with that inconvenient ray of sunlight, George had instead cried: "Block out that infernal sun!"

As now you understand, to Robert the Robot's neural network (his robotic mind), George's final set of instructions was something like this:

"The most important thing I have to tell you is to block out that infernal sun!"

And that is what Robert was trying to do. He first shut all the blinds and shutters and curtains, but, obviously, most window blinds and shades let in a little bit of light, even when they're closed. George's instructions had been clear: "Block out that infernal sun!" And so Robert had started sealing the windows with the blankets and cardboard and even sheets of plywood.

Of course, the situation was very unfortunate because Robert really was looking forward to having some time to himself—to read books and watch movies and relax. And George wanted to tell Robert to relax and to not take things so literally and seriously.

Sadly, the end result was that Robert was not relaxing, and *he was* taking things literally and very seriously.

After Robert had sealed up all the windows with duct tape and blankets and plywood, his exquisitely sensitive, robotic-vision sensors (in other words, his eyes) detected minute quantities of light leaking through the cardboard and blankets and around the strips of tape. There was also a faint line of light along the bottom of the front and back and side doors. And this was to say nothing of the laboratory and fabrication facility, where there were many large windows, each of which would have to be blocked and sealed.

What can I do now? thought Robert. *There is still so much sunlight leaking into the house. I'll never block it all. Clearly, it is very important to George that all of the light is blocked, but this will be a very challenging task.*

And so Robert began a new plan. He would order construction materials and lumber, and he would remodel the entire house and the lab and the fabrication facility so that there were no windows and no openings that would permit light to enter. It would probably take at least a month, maybe more.

Just at that moment, the mailman dropped the daily mail through the slot in the front door. A few envelopes and magazines fell to the floor with a soft thump. Robert knew he must sort and set aside the mail for processing by George upon his return, but a wide beam of sunlight also flooded into the house, reminding Robert of how many ways there were for sunlight to find its way in.

Then he thought of something else. What about all the sunlight outside?

Robert sat down in the darkness and his neural network began to heat up.

Now I understand why George said this was the most important thing he had to tell me, thought Robert. *This task is much bigger than preventing sunlight from entering the house.*

Robert stood up. He knew what he had to do.

I must block the sun itself!

CHAPTER 4

An instant or two after Hannah had declared that Mr. Meowgi hadn't run away from home, Mia noticed that Hannah was wearing a rather fetching, rainbow-colored, zipper-pouched fanny pack.

"Hannah," said Mia. "I like your fanny pack. When did you get it?"

"Thank you for noticing," said Hannah. "It's brand new."

"No more big purse?" asked Mia, pointing at the fanny pack.

"Right," replied Hannah, unzipping the pack's main compartment. "This fanny pack is more hands-free, allowing me to be more efficient in the solving of mysteries." She reached into the pack and produced her bubble pipe.

Hannah blew a bunch of bubbles, which were

buffeted on the breeze.

Lacy spoke up. "Why did you say that Mr. Meowgi didn't run away from home?" she asked.

Mia and Hannah turned to her, as if they'd somehow forgotten she was there.

"Ah, yes," said Hannah. "The game is afoot!"

"What game?" asked Mia. "I thought we weren't playing games today."

"Yeah, and why is it a foot?" asked Lacy.

"You misunderstand me," said Hannah. "When I say, 'the game is afoot,' I mean that we have a mystery to solve. We have a new case to investigate."

"Well, why didn't you just say *that?*" asked Mia.

"Because it's much more *dramatic* to say, 'the game is afoot!'" replied Hannah. "It's something Sherlock Holmes always says."

"Okay, so, why do you think that my cat did not run away from home?" Lacy asked again.

"Elementary, dear Lacy!" cried Hannah. She blew another bevy of bubbles. "First, Mr. Meowgi has been in your family for ten years, has he not?"

"Yes," said Lacy.

"That is a long time," said Hannah. "And it makes it unlikely that the cat has simply wandered away. Many kittens get lost or run away, but older cats are less likely to do so."

Lacy and Mia nodded.

"Secondly!" Hannah continued, holding up two fingers. "Mr. Meowgi is a very *large* feline, is he not?"

Lacy nodded.

"So, it's safe to assume that Mr. Meowgi is also lazy, listless, and lethargic. This means he couldn't go very far, and he'd be easy to find. And yet, you've searched extensively, and Mr. Meowgi is nowhere to be found."

Lacy and Mia nodded some more.

"Thirdly!" said Hannah, holding up three fingers. "Lacy, you told me that Mr. Meowgi's collar was found in the driveway of your home, did you not?"

"I did," said Lacy. She put her hand into her pocket and brought out a blue pet collar lined with rhinestones, a bell, and a nametag with *Mr. Meowgi* printed on it. Hannah took the collar from Lacy and held it up to examine.

"Lacy," said Hannah, "would you mind telling me why Mr. Meowgi removed his collar before he left? More importantly, *how* did he remove the collar?"

Lacy obviously hadn't considered this. "Yeah, that's a good point," she said, putting her hand on her forehead. "It's unbuckled. He certainly doesn't know how to do *that*."

"I thought so," said Hannah. "Someone must have removed it during the catnapping!"

Lacy's eyes were wide. "Wow. You're right! I didn't think of that!"

"Lacy," said Hannah, "with me on your side, you'll never have to think for yourself again. I believe you mentioned you had photographs of Mr. Meowgi for us to use in our investigation?"

"Yes," replied Lacy. She reached into her pocket again. "I have a few different pictures. Here they are. You may keep them."

"Thank you," said Hannah. "This will be very helpful. Well, my friends," Hannah went on, checking her wristwatch, "it's suppertime. I recommend retiring to our respective repasts."

"You recommend retiring to our *whats*?" asked Mia.

"Our respective *repasts*," repeated Hannah. "A *repast* is a *meal*. In other words, I think we should go *home* to have *dinner*."

"Why didn't you just say *that*?" said Mia, rolling her eyes. "Let me guess. More dramatic?"

"Precisely," said Hannah. "Precisely right."

CHAPTER 5

THE NEXT MORNING, no one at Mia's house was surprised when they detected a deranged *ding-dong-ding-dong-ding-dong-ding*ing at their doorbell. They didn't need to check the doorbell camera app to know it was Hannah. However, if they *had* checked the doorbell camera, they might have been surprised at what they saw.

The camera didn't show Hannah at all. Instead, it showed a large purple orb hovering and wavering in the air.

Hannah herself stood immediately *behind* the rubbery wobbling orb, which was an enormous bubble of bubblegum that Hannah was blowing. It may have been the biggest bubble she'd ever been able to blow. It first grew to the size of an ordinary

31

orange, then that of a softball, and then a birthday balloon.

Mia heard the ringing and knew it meant Hannah had arrived. Nevertheless, in the next room, Mia's sister, Miley, felt it necessary to shout, "Mia! Hannah's here!"

"I know, I know," Mia muttered as she jogged down the hall.

As Mia passed the kitchen, her father spotted her and said, "Mia, sounds like Hannah."

"I know, I know," Mia repeated.

As Mia reached the front door, she saw her mother, who was on the couch reading a newspaper. She peeked over the top of the newspaper and said, "Hannah's at the door, Mia."

"I know, I know," said Mia as she opened the front door.

On the porch, of course, was Hannah, peeling purple pieces of bubblegum from her sunglasses.

"Hi, Hannah," said Mia.

"Mia?" said Hannah. "Is that you? My vision is temporarily impaired. Did you see that bubble?"

"No," said Mia. "I didn't need to look at the camera to know who was ringing."

"That," Hannah stated sadly, "is a shame. It was of prodigious proportions."

Hannah paused her gum-clearing activity to grope into her new rainbow fanny pack. From the pack she removed the photos of Mr. Meowgi and held them out to Mia.

"Here," said Hannah. "These are the pictures of Mr. Meowgi. Familiarize yourself with his appearance. It shouldn't be difficult. He's unusually ugly."

Mia took the photos and looked at them.

It's well known that cats are some of the most beautiful creatures on planet Earth. Lions are massive and majestic. Leopards are sleek and mysterious. And even ordinary house cats can be irresistibly beautiful, with their soft fur, big eyes, and pert little noses.

Mr. Meowgi was not majestic, mysterious, or beautiful. He was big and misshapen, with short, stubby legs and a tremendous belly. His tufts of brown and orange fur stuck out at all angles. His crossed eyes were a sickly shade of yellow and were always partially shut, giving the impression that he was slightly dissatisfied. His whiskers were not straight and even; they were crookedly and crazily bent and all were of different lengths. Mr. Meowgi's whole face was dimpled inward into a permanent scowl.

Hannah plucked the last of the lingering gum from her glasses. "To be honest, Mia, if that were my cat, I'm not sure I'd want him back."

"That's not a very nice thing to say," said Mia. "And looks aren't that important, anyway."

"I suppose you're right," said Hannah. "And we've agreed to take on the case, so there's no turning back now. Speaking of which—Mia, why in blazes are you so dressed up? We're about to embark on a full day of investigating the Mystery of the Missing Mr. Meowgi! What's with the dress and hair bow?"

"Hannah," replied Mia with a sigh, "do you know what day it is today?"

"Don't be silly, Mia," said Hannah, lifting her shades up onto her forehead. "I wouldn't be much of a detective if I couldn't keep track of what *day* it was. It's Sunday."

"Right," said Mia. "And do you know what I do on Sunday?"

"Ah, yes," said Hannah. "Church. I had quite forgotten this ritual of yours. Well, is your mother at home?"

"Yes," replied Mia, motioning for Hannah to come in. "She's here in the living room."

Hannah stepped in and approached Mia's mother, Mrs. Maria Miller.

"Mrs. Miller, I must appeal to you once again to release Mia from her Sunday obligations. We have a missing cat on our hands. Or, perhaps I should say we have a cat which is missing and is therefore *not* on our hands. And because the cat is so—" Hannah was about to say "ugly," but did not want to give offense. Instead, she said, "*unique* in his appearance, I'm

35

afraid no one else will bother to look for him. Mia, show her the pictures."

Mia handed the photos of Mr. Meowgi to her mother.

Mrs. Miller grimaced. "Hm," she murmured, handing the photos back to Mia. "If this were my cat, I'm not sure I'd want him back."

"Mom!" cried Mia.

"That's what *I* said, Mrs. Miller," said Hannah. "So, can Mia be excused from church today?"

"No," said Mrs. Miller. "I admire you for helping to find the missing cat, but Mia has to come to church. However, I'll tell you what we'll do."

"What's that?" asked Hannah.

"We'll say a prayer for Mr. Meowgi."

"Couldn't hurt, I guess," admitted Hannah.

Mia walked Hannah back to the front door.

"This cat isn't exactly gorgeous," said Mia, passing the photos back to Hannah, "but beauty *is* in the eye of the beholder. Lacy's family obviously doesn't think Mr. Meowgi is ugly."

"Yes, you're right, Mia," said Hannah, "but I can't stay to discuss it. The game is afoot!"

CHAPTER 6

Robert the Robot quickly came up with a plan to completely block out the sun. As mentioned, Robert thought his inventor, George Gevol, who was vacationing in the Australian Outback, wanted him to block out the sun. George really did not want this, but even so, Robert's plan was a good one. It would require a lot of construction, fabrication, and computer configuration, but Robert's plan was proceeding in a satisfactory way.

That's what he *thought,* anyway.

Robert knew the plan would also require lots of help, so he had re-configured and re-programmed all the other robots around the house so that they could help.

For example, George had invented a robot to wash the outside of all the windows in the house.

The robot's name was Suds McGee. He had many arms for efficiently cleaning and wiping and drying windows. Suds's legs were also extendable, up to two hundred feet, so that he could easily reach the high windows of the fabrication facility and the windows high up on the second story of the house.

Robert had re-programmed Suds to help with the sun-blocking project—his numerous arms and long legs would be very useful in building the tall structure that Robert was planning.

George had designed and built another robot that mowed the lawn and did other yard work. Her name was Linda Clipper. Robert re-programmed Linda to clear away all the shrubs, trees, and grass from the site where Robert planned to build the tall structure.

The other robots that George had built for various purposes around the house had been likewise re-fitted and re-purposed to help with the big project.

And so Robert the Robot was very pleased at his progress.

George will be so impressed when he gets back from Australia, thought Robert.

By now you're probably wondering about Robert the Robot's project. How did he plan to block out the *entire* sun? You're probably thinking, the sun is a mass of incandescent gas, a gigantic nuclear furnace! You're probably thinking that, if the sun were hollow, a million Earths could fit inside. You're probably thinking that no matter if you can see it or not, the sun is shining down on the Earth, providing heat and light. You're also probably thinking that the sun isn't anywhere close to Earth—it's about 93 million miles away!

So, you're wondering how one robot could make a plan to block out the very massive, powerful, and distant sun (which is, technically, a star known as "Sol")?

Robert, of course, had also thought of these questions. And this is what he concluded:

Elementary, thought Robert. *I shall build a parasol.*

A parasol, as you may already know, looks a lot like an umbrella, but instead of waterproof fabric to block rain or snow, a parasol is made of cloth intended to block the harsh heat and light of the sun. In fact, the word "parasol" is made up of two parts: the first part, "para" means "protects against," and the second part, "sol," as mentioned previously, is another word for "the sun." In other words, "parasol" refers to something that "protects against the sun."

(Interestingly, the meaning of the word "umbrella" is actually very similar to that of "parasol.")

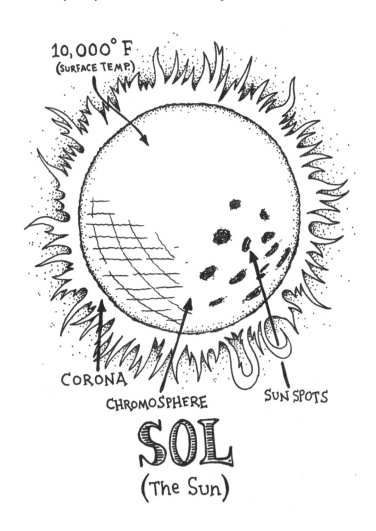

10,000° F
(SURFACE TEMP.)

CORONA

CHROMOSPHERE

SUN SPOTS

SOL
(The Sun)

The parasol that Robert planned to build would be no ordinary parasol. An ordinary parasol wouldn't do. If Robert wanted to really block out that "infernal" sun, he couldn't just hold up a parasol to hold over George's head. No, he must block all sunshine falling on the house. And even a parasol large enough to keep George's house in the dark wasn't enough. Because what if George wanted to go outside for a walk around the block to stretch his legs (as he often did)? Or what if George needed to pop down to Kramer's Grocery Store for a frozen pizza (as he also often did)?

Robert concluded that he must block the sun from shining on the *entire town* of Cardwick. And so Robert planned to build a very tall and enormous parasol that would cast a shadow over Cardwick, keeping the town in permanent darkness. The parasol would be attached to the top of a tower that moved on hinges and pulleys, blocking out the sun as it crossed the sky from sunup to sunset.

Did Robert know that, without the sun, the sunflowers in Mr. Norris' garden would die? Did Robert understand that, without the sun, all the vegetables in Mrs. Lemon's garden would shrivel away? Did he realize that, without the sun, even George Gevol's own house plants would turn brown and perish?

Yes. He knew all of this.

Robert had all kinds of knowledge nestled in his neural network (his brain), including information about photosynthesis, which is how plants eat, grow, and live. Plants need water, carbon dioxide, and sunlight to live. If a plant cannot get one or more of those ingredients, it will not be able to photosynthesize, and it will eventually die.

However, don't forget that Robert's neural network was still developing, still learning, and so he was under the mistaken impression that George's request to "block out that infernal sun" was "the most important thing" George had ever told Robert. And so Robert simply assumed (incorrectly) that flowers and vegetables and house plants were *less* important.

With the other household robots as his helpers, Robert began construction. Soon a tall and ominous tower began to rise from George Gevol's backyard.

CHAPTER 7

AFTER SCHOOL ON MONDAY, Mia and Hannah got
on the bus for home. They sat in their assigned seats,
which meant that they weren't close enough to have
a quiet conversation, but Hannah got Mia's attention
anyway.

"Psst! Mia!" Hannah hissed at Mia. "Psst!"

Someone sitting near Hannah nudged someone
sitting near Mia. That person nudged Mia and
pointed to Hannah, and then Mia looked at Hannah.

"Mia! Psst!" Hannah hissed again.

"Hannah," replied Mia, her voice raised over the
bus noise. "What is it?"

"Do you know Morse Code?" Hannah said this
in a whisper that was somehow much louder than
her ordinary speaking voice.

"Who?" shouted Mia.

"Morse Code!" hissed Hannah, cupping her hands around her mouth.

"Is that the tough guy with the beard who does karate in the movies?" Mia shouted back.

"Not *Chuck Norris!*" Hannah whispered hysterically. "I said *Morse Code!*"

"I've never heard of him!" was Mia's shouted reply.

Hannah shut her eyes and pinched the bridge of her nose. Then she dug around in her rainbow fanny pack, removed the new evidence notebook, and quickly scrawled a note. Next, she ripped the page from the notebook, folded it up, and addressed it this way:

TO: MIA MILLER, SEAT 35, CARDWICK MIDDLE SCHOOL BUS 9—TOP SECRET

The note passed from hand to hand across School Bus 9 until it reached Mia, who opened it and read:

Dear Mia,

Morse Code is a system of dots and dashes often used to communicate in secret. I must talk with you about Mr. Meowgi's case, but we have yet to eliminate any suspects, including every single person here on Bus 9 (not to exclude Mr. Taylor, our driver) and so we should speak secretly for now.

So, do you know Morse Code?

Sincerely,

Hannah

Mia dug around in her backpack and found a pencil. She wrote a reply and sent it back across the bus. Hannah received the reply excitedly, opened it, and read it. Here's what it said:

My dearest Hannah,

No.

Yours truly,

Mia

Hannah appeared annoyed at this. She scribbled a reply to Mia's reply and sent it back. Mia opened it and read:

My most cherished Mia,

You didn't have to write that in a note and send it back. You could have just yelled, NO. For goodness sake, I'm just over here in seat 15.

With fond regards,

Hannah

Mia didn't know what else to say, so she shrugged sheepishly and shouted, "Why don't we just talk about it when we get off the bus? We only have a few miles to go!"

Hannah scribbled a new note, ripped it from the evidence notebook, addressed it to Mia, and sent it.

The note passed from hand to hand and finally to Mia. It read:

To my intrepid companion Mia,

Fine.

My respects to you and your family,

Hannah

A few miles later, Hannah and Mia got off the bus.

"I have lots of ideas about our case," said Hannah.

"What are they?" asked Mia.

"First, we must search the neighborhood around Lacy's house," replied Hannah.

"What?" replied Mia. "You said that Mr. Meowgi was most likely catnapped, and that we wouldn't have to search for him."

"Yes," answered Hannah. "The chances are slim that we'll find Mr. Meowgi by searching. However, we must be thorough, and that means we must conduct a search of our own."

"That'll take forever," complained Mia. "Days! Maybe weeks! Meanwhile, if Mr. Meowgi was catnapped, the probability of finding his catnappers grows smaller every day."

"Correct!" said Hannah, jabbing her finger into the air. "That is why *we* will *not* conduct the search, nor any other *human being*," said Hannah with a sly grin on her face.

"What are you talking about?" said Mia, knitting her eyebrows. "Who's going to do the search, instead? Space aliens?"

"No," answered Hannah. "That's not a bad idea, however. Aliens would probably have superior technology, which could be very useful to us. Here. Make a note in the evidence notebook. 'If we encounter any space aliens, ask them how they'd feel about helping out with our detective work'."

Mia took the notebook and jotted down the note. Then she said, "So, who—or what—is going to search for Mr. Meowgi?"

"Elementary, my dear Mia," answered Hannah. "A *robot* will conduct the search."

CHAPTER 8

When Mia and Hannah arrived at Hannah's house, Hannah showed Mia the robot she had mentioned earlier.

"This is the Drone-o-Graph A5000," Hannah explained. "It's my dad's aerial drone."

Mia looked at the device. It was made of sleek, black plastic and was roughly the size of a four-slice toaster, but unlike any toaster, the Drone-o-Graph A5000 was equipped with four tiny but powerful propellers and a photographic lens that faced downward.

Hannah explained, "We can use a remote control and computer programming to tell this thing to fly around anywhere we want. It's basically a flying robot."

"Wow, cool," breathed Mia.

"As it flies around, the drone will record high-resolution video of the whole place. We will then give the video file to Lacy. Mr. Meowgi is roughly the size of a juvenile grizzly bear, so if he's anywhere within a couple miles of Lacy's house, he should be easy to spot from above. When Lacy watches the video, she can pause, zoom in, fast forward, and rewind—she can even watch in slow-motion and infra-red."

"Brilliant!" said Mia. "With the Drone-o-Graph A5000, no one has to walk around all the blocks, wander through the parks, search around yards, or crisscross any farm fields! Lacy can search from the comfort of her computer!"

"Precisely!" said Hannah. "Meanwhile, you and I will be sleuthing for clues down new avenues of investigation."

Hannah's father, Iggi, helped Hannah and Mia get the Drone-o-Graph A5000 prepared for flight. Iggi had long blonde hair and a kind face, and he loved computers and technology. He used a cable to plug the drone into his computer, and then he consulted electronic aerial maps from the Internet to program the drone's flight path.

"I want the drone to fly over everything within

two-miles of Lacy's house," said Hannah, staring at the computer monitor.

"Okay," said Iggi as he typed and clicked, "we'll program it to fly directly above all these streets."

"What if Mr. Meowgi is under a tree or hidden by grass?" asked Mia.

"Lacy will be able to use the infra-red spectrum, which will show Mr. Meowgi's heat," said Iggi. "That should help her see under bushes and grass and trees."

"Gadzooks," said Mia and Hannah together.

"I'll also program it to fly over open areas like the parks and farm fields within the search area," Iggi added.

"Hey, what if there are telephone poles or tall trees in the way?" asked Mia. "Won't the A5000 crash into them?"

"No," said Iggi. "Telephone poles, cell phone towers, and tall buildings are all known about on the Internet and recorded on the electronic maps. So, the drone will fly around them."

"Amazing," said Mia.

Soon the Drone-o-Graph A5000 was programmed and ready to fly.

"All right," said Iggi to Hannah and Mia. "Take the Drone-o-Graph A5000 outside. Use this remote-control unit to get it airborne. When it's about a hundred feet up, press this button on the remote control."

The button was labeled, *EXECUTE FLIGHT PROGRAM.*

"After that," said Iggi, with a shrug, "it will fly the search pattern on its own and record the video. If it needs new batteries, the drone will come back and beep at you. When it has completed the search flight, it will land here at the house again. Good luck, kids!"

The Drone-o-Graph was simply astounding. Hannah got it airborne with the remote control, and then turned to Mia and said, "Execute flight program!"

Mia saluted and pressed the *EXECUTE FLIGHT PROGRAM* button, and the drone immediately flew away in the direction of Shady Lane and Lacy's house. The two sleuths watched through the monitor on the remote-control unit as the A5000 carefully flew over the streets and yards of the search area. This took almost an hour and required a change of batteries, but this was much, much faster than biking up and down the streets and sidewalks.

Hannah and Mia watched as the drone returned to them after it had completed its flight.

"Here comes the A5000!" said Hannah, pointing into the distance.

"Is it all right? It looks like it's flying kinda crookedy," Mia observed.

Hannah knew "crookedy" wasn't a word, but she knew what Mia meant. The drone was swerving and swooping woozily, and Hannah thought she saw smoke pouring from one of the propellers. She unzipped her rainbow fanny pack, reached inside, and produced a set of small binoculars. She peered nervously through them in the direction of the drone. "You're right, Mia! It's damaged!"

Soon the two sleuths could hear the drone sputtering and buzzing miserably.

"It must have hit something!" said Hannah.

"But your dad said it would know how to fly around obstacles," Mia suggested.

The drone approached on a sickly zig-zag course. Sparks and smoke were coming from one of the propellers, but after a few more minutes, the Drone-o-Graph A5000 managed to land safely on the driveway of Hannah's house.

CHAPTER 9

ROBERT THE ROBOT surveyed the wreckage of his sun-blocking parasol tower. It lay twisted and strewn across the backyard. At first, Robert wondered how a drone the size of a toaster could do so much damage, but he soon figured it out.

Suds McGee, the window-washing robot, had been redesigned so that his legs were *three* hundred feet long, and he'd been working on the highest part of the tower. However, Suds wasn't accustomed to the longer leg units yet, so he was already a bit wobbly. As Suds worked on the tower and struggled to keep his balance, he heard a buzzing sound behind him, and he turned around just in time to see the Drone-o-Graph A5000 heading straight at him. Suds tried to duck, but he was simply too shaky on the new leg units, and the drone hit Suds right between the eyes. This didn't hurt Suds very much, but it did nothing to help his balance. Suds began to tip, lean, and careen. He grabbed the parasol tower to steady himself, but it was no use. Suds collapsed, bringing down the tower in the process.

Unfortunately, two other robots were involved, too. The first was Heavy D, a stout robot designed to move heavy materials. Heavy D was bringing a big load of aluminum beams to Suds. The other robot was Linda Clipper, who was trying to keep the construction site free of weeds. Both robots were buried beneath the collapsing tower.

Robert was very upset to discover that all three robots—Suds McGee, Heavy D, and Linda Clipper —were totally demolished!

Fortunately, no one was seriously hurt.

Yes, you read that right—the three robots were demolished but not seriously hurt. George's robots did not feel physical pain the way people do, and George's robots could be repaired and even rebuilt completely. As long as their neural networks (their brains) were undamaged, the robots were fine. George was always sure to put his robots' neural networks inside steel cases that were practically indestructible. So, Robert the Robot was upset, but only because Suds, Heavy, and Linda would have to be rebuilt. That would take extra time away from the project.

In other words, not only would Robert have to start over on his project, he would have to rebuild the three demolished robots first, and *then* start over.

This is truly awful, thought Robert.

CHAPTER 10

HANNAH'S FATHER, Iggi, was only slightly disappointed that his Drone-o-Graph A5000 had been damaged during the search flight. "I can repair the drone with spare parts," he told Hannah and Mia, "but I'm confused about what happened."

"Can you look at the drone video to find out?" asked Mia.

"I did that," said Iggi, "but the camera lens wasn't facing forward when the mishap occurred, so the video isn't very helpful. The drone collided with something very high up in the air, but according to the city maps, there are no towers or buildings in that area."

"Sorry, Dad," said Hannah. "We didn't mean for the Drone-o-Graph A5000 to become a casualty."

"Well, that's a mystery for another time," said

Iggi. "For now, you two better continue your investigation into Mr. Meowgi's disappearance. Here's the memory chip with the search-flight video."

Hannah gladly accepted the tiny memory chip and exclaimed, "To the bikes! Let's deliver this video to Lacy, and at the same time, we'll ask her to give *us* some video footage in return."

"What do you mean by that?" asked Mia.

"I'll explain on the way!" said Hannah, heading for the door.

As they pedaled to Lacy's house, Hannah told Mia about how her giant, record-breaking bubble of purple bubblegum had led to an idea about how to find Mr. Meowgi's catnapper.

"Lacy's house has a doorbell camera, too," explained Hannah. "And most of these doorbell cameras keep past doorbell encounters for a matter of weeks or even months."

"Ah ha!" said Mia. "So, if we get Lacy's doorbell camera footage, we might be able to see who was hanging around her house when Mr. Meowgi disappeared."

"Precisely right," said Hannah.

They both pedaled a little faster. Within minutes they pulled up on their bikes at Lacy's house and knocked on Lacy's door.

"Hi, Mia and Hannah," said Lacy. "Do you have the drone video for me to search?"

"We sure do," said Hannah, holding up the drone's memory chip. "But we're going to need some video from you, too."

Lacy said she didn't understand this, and so Hannah quickly repeated everything to Lacy. Then the three of them checked with Lacy's parents, Lulu and Larry, and soon the three girls were seated in front of yet another laptop, watching doorbell camera footage.

Hannah pointed to a collection of video files. "These are from the day *before* Mr. Meowgi's disappearance."

In the first video, taken on the morning before Mr. Meowgi went missing, a man in a blue shirt, gray shorts, and a sun hat could be seen walking up to the front door of Lacy's house. His image warped comically in the fish-eye lens.

"That's just our mail carrier," said Lacy, pointing as the man in the video came right up to the door, dropped some mail through the slot, and then continued up the sidewalk.

"We must leave no stone unturned, Lacy," said Hannah, handing Mia the evidence notebook. "Mia, write down, 'Person of interest 1: Mail carrier'."

Mia did as Hannah said.

The next video was also captured the day before Mr. Meowgi was reported missing. However, in this video, no one actually came to the door. It was a lady in lime-green athletic clothes with her hair in a pony-tail who simply jogged along the sidewalk past Lacy's house.

"Doorbell cameras are triggered by movement," Hannah explained, "so, sometimes it records people just passing by. Lacy, do you know this person?"

Lacy narrowed her eyes and peered at the computer monitor. "She looks familiar," said Lacy, "but I'm not sure who it is."

"Hey, she looks familiar to me, too," said Mia.

"Okay," said Hannah, "write down, 'Person of interest 2: Jogger lady with cute green jogging clothes and ponytail, who looks familiar'."

Mia jotted down the note.

There were other videos from that day, but they only showed Lacy's family coming and going from the house.

Next the trio watched the videos from the day Mr. Meowgi actually vanished. The first video again showed the mail carrier, with his blue and gray uniform and his sun hat.

"Ah ha!" cried Hannah, leaning in for a better

look. "This guy again! I'm definitely going to want to interview *him*."

"Hannah," said Mia. "He's dropping off more mail. See?"

"I didn't say he's a suspect," Hannah said sternly. "I simply want to speak with him. We must leave no stone or mail carrier unturned!"

Then the lady with the cute ponytail and lime-green jogging outfit flitted past the house.

"Her again!" cried Hannah. "We must find out who she is!"

There were more videos of Lacy's family entering and exiting the house, but the next video showed a little old lady coming up the walkway to the front door. She wore a flowered dress, and her curly hair was grayish-blue. She carried what looked like a dinner plate covered with plastic wrap.

"That's Mrs. Beechtree," said Lacy. "She lives down the street."

"What's that she's carrying?" said Hannah.

"Probably cookies," said Lacy. "She makes a lot of cookies and gives them to all her neighbors."

"I see," said Hannah in a low tone. "Mia?"

"I know," said Mia. "Person of interest 3: Mrs. Beechtree."

"Add a footnote," said Hannah, "'Cookies'."

Mia wrote down the information.

None of the other videos from around the time of Mr. Meowgi's alleged abduction showed anyone else except family members, but Hannah was satisfied with their afternoon of sleuthing.

"We now have three persons of interest to investigate," said Hannah.

"But what about a catnapper who might have come in through the back?" asked Mia. "Or snuck in through a window?"

"I'm afraid we can't be sure if anything like that happened," said Hannah. "So, we'll have to investigate the people on the video and see where they lead us."

CHAPTER 11

IT HAD GOTTEN QUITE late in the evening, so Mia and Hannah gave Lacy the video footage from the Drone-o-Graph A5000, said their goodbyes, and went home. However, Hannah and Mia returned to Lacy's house the next day after school.

"Hannah," enquired Mia, "why are we searching around Lacy's yard? We don't expect to find Mr. Meowgi out here, do we?"

"No," said Hannah. "I'm sure the Lamberts searched this yard very thoroughly, but only for the cat *himself*. Today, we're searching for *clues*."

Hannah then reached into the rainbow fanny pack and produced her bubble pipe, magnifying glass, and the evidence notebook. The bubble pipe she clamped in her teeth, the magnifying glass she held up to her eye, and the notebook she handed to Mia, along with a small pencil.

"Like what?" asked Mia. "What clues?"

"Well, that's the paradox of clues, Mia," said Hannah, using the magnifying glass to examine the grass. "You never know what they are until you've found them."

"Can you give me a *clue* about what kind of *clues* we're looking for?" Mia complained.

A string of small bubbles trailed behind Hannah as she wandered through the yard. "You know. We're looking for the usual, by which I mean the *unusual*. Anything out of the ordinary."

"What about this?" asked Mia.

Hannah turned to look. "Uh, that's a bicycle, Mia. It's not out of the ordinary. In fact, a bicycle is precisely *within* the ordinary."

"It's got a flat tire," mumbled Mia with a shrug.

"Look harder," said Hannah.

The two sleuths walked around to the side of the Lambert house. Hannah produced a soapy profusion of pipe bubbles and then proclaimed, "Hellooo, what have we here?"

"Uh, it's a garbage can, Hannah," said Mia, wrinkling up her nose. "The only thing out of the ordinary about *that* is the stink."

It was indeed a garbage can, the kind made of steel, covered by a round lid with a handle in the center. (And indeed it did stink.)

"Mia, have you any idea how many crimes have been solved by investigators looking through trash?" said Hannah. She wrinkled her nose at the odor, too, but then she stepped tentatively over to the garbage can.

"Don't do it," said Mia with a shudder. "It's too gross!"

Hannah unzipped her rainbow fanny pack, dug around inside, and traded her bubble pipe and magnifying glass for a pair of purple latex dish-washing gloves. "You're right about the smell," admitted Hannah, "but, as always, I've come prepared!" She waved the gloves in the air.

"I can't watch!" squealed Mia, clapping her hands over her eyes.

With both of her gloved hands, Hannah grabbed the round lid. After only one moment of further hesitation, she pulled the lid away and then looked inside. Mia peeked through her fingers. Whatever Hannah saw in the garbage can must have been incredible. Hannah blinked a few times, bent down a little, and looked closer.

Then Hannah stood up and flung the garbage can lid to one side as though it were an enormous boomerang. It sailed through the air, across the Lambert's yard, and over their back fence, where it apparently caught a favorable breeze and continued its flight straight and true into a neighboring yard.

"Gadzooks!" cried Hannah, regarding the contents of the garbage can with amazement.

"What's in there?" said Mia. "Something disgusting? Revolting? Nauseating?"

"It's a clue!" cried Hannah. She reached in and carefully lifted it up.

It was an ordinary tuna fish can.

It was short and round, and on the label was a cartoon tuna fish wearing glasses. Hannah held the tuna can pinched between her thumb and index finger at the end of her outstretched arm, as though it might contain a dead mouse. After turning it this way and that to give it a good looking-over, Hannah set the can on the ground, and the two girls crouched down for a better look.

"How is this a clue?" asked Mia, crouching next to Hannah.

"It's a tuna fish can," Hannah replied, pointing to the can with a gloved finger.

"So?"

"So, if this was a *succotash* can, I wouldn't be interested in it, even though I do love succotash. But this is a tuna fish can, and as everyone knows, cats *love* canned tuna fish."

"That's true," said Mia. "But that doesn't make it out of the ordinary, does it?"

"No," asked Hannah, "But there *is* something out of the ordinary about *this* can. Can you figure out what it is?"

"Hmm," Mia answered, tilting her head and squinting her eyes. "Well, there is actually quite a bit of tuna left inside."

"Very good, Mia!" Hannah purred. "I noticed that, too. Now, *ordinarily,* when a person opens a tuna can, say, to make a tuna fish sandwich, they empty it out. They scrape all the tuna out of the can with a spoon. But most of the tuna was left in this can. This can is *out* of the ordinary. This can is a *clue.*"

"I see," Mia said softly.

"Write down the details, please," said Hannah. "Include the brand—it's the kind with the little blue fish who wears glasses."

Mia made the necessary notes, including a sketch of the discarded can, with the fish on the label and the tuna remnants inside. Hannah transferred the tuna can back to the garbage can. She then removed her gloves with a loud rubbery snapping and tossed those in the garbage can, too.

Hannah looked around and said, "That's funny.

Where's the lid to this garbage can? It was here just a moment ago."

Mia put away the evidence notebook, then looked around but couldn't find the lid, either.

"How odd," said Hannah. "Well, there is much to do and we mustn't tarry. Come, Mia."

Mia followed Hannah to the front door. Hannah rang the bell, and Lacy answered.

"Hello, Lacy," said Hannah. "Have you spotted Mr. Meowgi on the drone video?"

"No," said Lacy, sounding a little sad. "But I'm searching very carefully."

"Excellent," said Hannah. "We've finished searching your yard. I have good news and bad news."

Lacy's eyes opened wide. "What's the good news?"

"I may have unearthed an important clue," Hannah replied calmly, "but I must ask you, on what day is your garbage picked up each week?"

"Thursday," said Lacy. "It's my job to take the trash can out to the curb."

"I see," said Hannah. "Very good. Now, I must look through your kitchen."

"Oh," said Lacy. "Okay. Come right in."

Without further chit-chat, Hannah breezed into

the Lambert's kitchen and began opening and searching the cupboards and drawers. She opened cupboards that were up high, drawers that were down low, and vice versa.

Lacy leaned over to Mia and whispered, "What's she looking for?"

"She'll know when she finds it," replied Mia.

After opening a cupboard where the Lambert family apparently kept all their canned goods, Hannah breathed, "Eureka!"

The other two girls came to Hannah's side and stared wide-eyed into the cupboard.

"Mia," said Hannah, gesturing to the cans, "do you see what I see?"

"Uh huh," said Mia. "The Lamberts buy canned tuna fish with a mermaid on the label."

"Please make a note of it," said Hannah.

Mia hurriedly scribbled down some notes and made another drawing.

"What's it mean?" asked Lacy.

"I'd love to tell you all about it, Lacy," said Hannah. "But the game is afoot, and we must be off. We'll be in touch. Mia! To the bikes!"

Mia and Hannah headed quickly for the door.

"Wait!" cried Lacy.

The two sleuths turned back to face Lacy.

"What was the bad news?" Lacy asked.

"Ah," said Hannah. "I nearly forgot. During our search of your backyard, I apparently misplaced your garbage can lid. I'll come back later to find it, but until then I hope you're not too inconvenienced."

CHAPTER 12

GEORGE WILL BE SO *pleased when he returns from Australia,* thought Robert the Robot. *He will be relaxed and refreshed and rested. He will have many souvenirs to show and tales to tell.*

Robert went out through the back door to look at his new project, the one he had started after his parasol tower had met such an unfortunate end.

Not only will George have had a happy holiday, thought Robert, *but the entire earth will be enveloped in total darkness. George will be very pleased, indeed.*

With his purple gleaming eyes, Robert gazed fondly at the missile he and the other robots had built. It stood stately on the launching pad, smooth and sleek, with a nose-cone as shiny and sharp as a needle. The architecture was absolutely aerodynamic, and the four fins were fitted to the fuselage in very fine fashion.

And it was aimed directly at the sun (a.k.a., Sol).

Robert hadn't had much time to design and build this rocket—only a few days—but he did have access to George's fabrication facility, which was state-of-the-art. It's also important to keep in mind that Robert was a robot, and so he did not require rest, and he had an entire team of other robots to help him.

They all came together and worked hard for the common goal that united them: to destroy the sun.

But even more importantly, Robert had the advantage of an absolutely, absurdly advanced brain, his neural network. Robert's neural network had not yet learned about taking things too literally, or taking things too far. However, Robert's brain *had* been programmed to know everything about science, and that included rocket science. And so Robert was able to quickly build one of the fastest and most destructive missiles ever conceived. It would fly into the heart of the sun, cause a massive nuclear reaction, and the sun would go out like an old light bulb. Yes, this would plunge the whole solar system into a deadly darkness colder than ice, but Robert's job would be done.

It might be a good idea to pause here for a reminder that Robert the Robot was not an evil, wicked, or even mean robot. He was just very misguided.

And so, Robert walked out into George's backyard and prepared to launch the missile.

The other robots gathered around to watch— Suds McGee, Linda Clipper, Heavy D, and all the others. They were all very proud of the work they'd done. But there was no speech or applause. There was not even a dramatic countdown. These robots didn't do things like that. They just wanted to see the rocket rip through the sky on the way to the sun. And so the ceremony was quite simple. Robert walked out of the house and over to the launching platform.

Then he pressed the launch button.

The rocket motors ignited and snowy white smoke billowed up around the platform. Then the rocket began to lift off. It was slow at first, but it was supposed to start slow. Only when it had reached one hundred feet or so would it really start to accelerate.

Success at last, thought Robert. *There are no problems with this plan.*

But then a problem arose.

From out of nowhere, something came hurtling across the sky. It was round and appeared to be made of steel, but it was also rather dingy and dented. It flew through the air like a flying saucer directly at Robert's rocket. As the rocket reached roughly twenty feet of altitude, the round rotating object struck the rocket and then ricocheted away!

The rocket still lifted off. The rocket still roared into the blue. This resulted in a new rash of U.F.O. reports, but the authorities did not take them very seriously (Cardwick was famous for its unverified U.F.O. sightings). However, even though the rocket appeared to fly straight and true, the mysterious flying disc of dingy, dented steel had diverted the rocket by one centimeter. Robert knew this, and he knew that the rocket plan was now hopelessly spoiled.

You see, when you aim a rocket at a target that is 93 million miles away, a course change of only one centimeter will cause the rocket to miss its target by hundreds of thousands of miles. Robert knew the rocket would miss the sun completely and fly harmlessly into empty space.

And all he could do was watch helplessly.

CHAPTER 13

ON WEDNESDAY, one week after Mr. Meowgi had gone missing, Mia told Hannah that she had to study for a test in science class and therefore could not go sleuthing after school. At the bus stop, the two sleuths prepared to part ways.

Hannah laid her hand on Mia's shoulder and said, "I'll miss your powers of perception, not to mention your precocious personality, but I'll sleuth solo and circle up with you soon."

"If I finish studying, I'll come and find you," Mia replied.

Hannah went straight home, grabbed her bike, and then pedaled to Mrs. Beechtree's house on Shady Lane to begin the day's detective duties.

Mrs. Beatrice Beechtree lived only a few houses from Lacy's house in a pretty little cottage with lovely flower beds. Hannah rang the doorbell. Mrs. Beechtree answered the door almost at once and seemed instantly overjoyed to have a visitor. She looked the same as she did in Lacy's doorbell video—curly gray-blue hair, little round glasses, and a flowered dress.

"Why, hello there!" she sang. "Come in! Come in!"

"Uh, ma'am," Hannah stammered as Mrs. Beechtree practically dragged her inside, "wouldn't you like to know who I am and the reason for my visit?"

"Oh, yes, I want to hear all about it, but first come in and let me get you some milk and cookies!" replied Mrs. Beechtree. "Then we can sit in the parlor, and you can tell me who you are and explain all about whatever it is you want to tell me all about."

Hannah shrugged and followed Mrs. Beechtree into the parlor, which was furnished with a soft-looking sofa and chairs and a little serving table. Mrs. Beechtree showed Hannah to a flowered, overstuffed chair.

"You make yourself comfortable," said Mrs. Beechtree. "I'll go and get the cookies and milk. They're all homemade and fresh-baked. What's your favorite kind of cookie?"

That's a good question, thought Hannah. *What* is *my favorite kind of cookie?*

"Do you have any triple-chocolate peppernuts?" Hannah asked brightly.

Mrs. Beechtree frowned a little and said, "Hm, no, I don't think so."

"How about frosted-almond icebox snicker-doodles?"

"Uhm, I don't think I have any of those, either," Mrs. Beechtree confessed.

"Okay then," said Hannah, "I'll just have some cherry-pistachio cardamom pinwheels, please."

"Dear me," said Mrs. Beechtree. "I'm afraid the only cookies I have on hand at the moment are chocolate chip, peanut butter, or oatmeal."

"Ooo, I love oatmeal cookies!" said Hannah, sitting up straight. "If, that is, they have lots of raisins in them."

A big smile appeared on Mrs. Beechtree's face. "Yes, my oatmeal cookies are baked with lots of raisins! I'll bring some! I won't be a minute!" She went to get the cookies.

Hannah looked around the room. She saw things one would expect to see in the cottage of an older lady. There was a vase of plastic flowers on a side table. There were magazines about how to crochet blankets. There were several crocheted blankets. On another side table there stood some framed photos of grandchildren. Hannah found it odd that one of the frames had been laid face-down, so that the photo could not be seen.

Maybe it's a grandkid who never comes to visit, Hannah thought, *or maybe one who's been naughty.*

Hannah didn't know why she assumed that the

naughty grandkid would be a "he," and she was about to tilt up the frame to see if she'd been right, when suddenly something significant caught her eye. In one corner of the parlor there stood a glass-enclosed bookshelf full of trophies and ribbons.

And the trophies and ribbons were from cat shows.

In case you've never been to one, a cat show is an event where lots of people bring their cats from all over to be judged by cat experts and admired by cat lovers. There are many varieties of cats, and they may win prizes for being the prettiest, the best behaved, or the most unique.

Hannah stood up from the overstuffed chair and walked over to see the trophies and ribbons. There were awards from many cat shows. There didn't seem to be any trophies or ribbons from recent shows, but there were many from previous years. Most of the awards read *FIRST PLACE* and *BEST IN SHOW*.

Just then, Mrs. Beechtree swept back into the room with a tray of oatmeal cookies and a glass of milk.

"Here you are, my dear!" she trilled. "Oh, I see you're admiring Pablo's awards."

Hannah turned and said, "Pablo?"

Mrs. Beechtree set down the tray of cookies and milk and said, "Yes, Pablo Picatso, my prize-winning Corellian Couch Cat. Come now, have some cookies. Baked fresh this morning!"

Hannah returned to the overstuffed chair and helped herself to the oatmeal cookies.

"These are delicious, Mrs. Beechtree," said Hannah.

"Thank you," said Mrs. Beechtree, obviously pleased. "Now then, would you like to tell me about yourself and why you've come?"

Hannah set down her plate of cookies, took a sip of milk, and then stood up. She made a slight bow and said, "Allow me to introduce myself. My name is Hannah, and I am Cardwick's foremost kid sleuth and private detective. I am completely self-taught and my name is spelled the same frontwards and backwards, with two H's, two A's, and two N's."

Mrs. Beechtree raised her eyebrows and said, "Go on."

After taking her seat again, Hannah said, "Mrs. Beechtree, before I state my business, may I ask about your cat, Pablo Picatso? According to your trophy case, Pablo is a very accomplished feline."

"Well, he *was*," said Mrs. Beechtree with a trace

of sadness. "He was a magnificently handsome cat, and he loved going to cat shows."

"What happened to Pablo?" asked Hannah. "That is, if you don't mind my asking."

"I don't mind," said Mrs. Beechtree, "although it's a very sad story. Pablo ran away about a year ago."

Hannah immediately replied, "I'm so sorry to hear that," but in her mind, she thought: *Another missing cat on the same street? There's a pattern here!*

"Thank you, dear," said Mrs. Beechtree. "I sure do miss him."

"Mrs. Beechtree," said Hannah, "it just so happens that I am here investigating the disappearance of Mr. Meowgi, a cat who until recently was in the care of your neighbors here on Shady Lane. You're acquainted with the Lamberts?"

"Another missing cat on the same street?" exclaimed Mrs. Beechtree. "Oh, no! I am so glad you've come to me. I'll be happy to help!"

"Well," said Hannah, "that's very generous of you, Mrs. Beechtree, but my team is already vigorously investigating the disappearance. In fact, I'm here to ask you a few que—"

"You say the cat's name is Mr. Meowgi?" asked Mrs. Beechtree urgently. From the drawer of a side table, she retrieved a pencil and a pad of paper. "And he belongs to the Lamberts?"

"Yes," stammered Hannah, "that is the cat's name but—"

"And have you searched for the cat?" Mrs. Beechtree continued. "How long has he been missing? Have you gone door to door and enquired about him?"

"Well," Hannah stuttered, "not exactly, but—"

"Have you hung up any posters or flyers with the cat's picture on them? Have you posted a picture on Facelook? Or Pinstagram?"

"You know, those are very good ideas, but—"

"Finish your cookies, sweetie," said Mrs. Beechtree, writing furiously on her notepad. "I'm outlining a plan to canvas the entire town to find the missing kitty. We must find him! We'll print flyers. Organize a search party! I've been through this before, and I know how heartbreaking it is. I'll take a batch of cookies to the Lambert's house today. It might help cheer them up, and I'll go over my plan to find Mr. Meowgi. Hannah, I'm sure you could be very helpful, too! Would you like to come with me?"

Hannah managed to say, "Mrs. Beechtree, I—" but Mrs. Beechtree had picked up her telephone and was dialing a number.

"Thank you for the cookies and milk," said Hannah. "I'll show myself out."

But Mrs. Beechtree didn't seem to notice that Hannah had spoken.

Hannah's head was spinning as she stepped off Mrs. Beechtree's porch and retrieved her bike to head homeward.

Two cats missing from the same street?

Was Mrs. Beechtree trying to take over the Mr. Meowgi case?

What about all the questions about tuna fish and doorbell cameras Hannah needed to ask?

These thoughts and a myriad more made a mess of Hannah's mind.

"I've got to get my head together," Hannah said to herself as she steered her bike sloppily down the sidewalk. "Where's Mia? I can't work alone like this!"

At that instant, from somewhere ahead, Hannah heard a man shout, "Whoa, Nellie!"

CHAPTER 14

HANNAH JAMMED ON HER BRAKES, and her bike skidded to an unsteady stop.

She'd nearly crashed into a mail carrier! Hannah had stopped just two feet short of running right over him with her bike. On his face he wore an expression that was partly amusement and partly terror.

"I'm so sorry!" cried Hannah. "I was spacing out, lost in thought!"

"Ah, near-misses are just part of the job," said the mailman. He'd dropped several parcels and letters, and he bent down to retrieve them.

"Let me help," said Hannah. She hopped off her bike. However, as she picked up the remaining envelopes, she noticed that this wasn't just any mail carrier—he was the Lambert's mail carrier!

"Thank you," said the man, placing the letters and packages into his bag.

"Pardon me for asking," said Hannah sheepishly. "but do you deliver mail to the houses on Shady Lane?"

"Yes, I do," said the man. "Why?"

"How fortuitous that I nearly flattened you!" said Hannah. Then she stood up straight and extended her hand. "Allow me to introduce myself. I'm Hannah, Cardwick's foremost kid sleuth. My name is spelled the same way backwards and forwards, and I've been hoping to speak with you!"

The mail carrier shook her hand and said, "Nice to meet you, Hannah. I'm Nelson Neederhouse. Why do you say it was fortuitous?"

"Well, Mr. Neederhouse," began Hannah, "I'm investigating a cat that has gone missing from a house on Shady Lane—I suppose you know the Lamberts? House number 108?"

"Of course," said Mr. Neederhouse, nodding his head. "A very nice family. I've seen that cat in the window. He's a big, ugly fellow. I heard he ran away, but I assumed he'd find his way home sooner or later."

"Mr. Meowgi didn't run away," said Hannah. "I'm convinced he was catnapped."

"You don't say," said Mr. Neederhouse. "Well, that's just terrible. But who would want such a lumpy, grumpy-looking pet? And why did you want to speak to me? You don't think I had anything to do with it, do you?"

"No, no," said Hannah, holding up a hand. "However, you visit 108 Shady Lane just about every day, and so I was wondering if you noticed anything out of the ordinary at that house, and specifically one week ago, last Wednesday, which is when Mr. Meowgi went missing."

Mr. Neederhouse looked thoughtfully into the air for a second or two. "No, nothing comes to mind," he said. "Who do you think might have taken Mr. Meowgi?"

"My prime suspect was Mrs. Beatrice Beechtree," said Hannah, "but when I tried to question her, she fed me cookies and tried to take over the whole case."

"Mrs. Beechtree?" said Mr. Neederhouse, looking surprised. "House number 213? Aw, she's just a harmless grandmother. She gives me fresh-baked cookies just about every week."

"Yes, well, I'm not sure what to think of her now," said Hannah, her eyes downcast. "My search for the solution seems to have stalled."

"You don't have any other suspects?" asked Mr. Neederhouse.

"Well, there is another person of interest, something of a mystery woman," said Hannah. "A jogger with a cute ponytail and lime-green jogging clothes, who was seen in video footage taken by the Lambert's doorbell camera."

"Oh, the lady with the big backpack?" said Mr. Neederhouse.

"Backpack?" said Hannah. "What backpack?"

"The jogger lady I saw was wearing a backpack," answered Mr. Neederhouse.

"When did you see her?" asked Hannah, her eyes suddenly big. "Last week? Tuesday or Wednesday?"

Mr. Neederhouse rubbed his chin. "Yeah," he said, "it was Tuesday and maybe Wednesday, too."

"And we're talking about the same jogger lady? Lime-green running suit? Cute ponytail?"

"Sure, sure," he replied, "*and* a large backpack."

"Oh, Mr. Neederhouse! I'm so glad I nearly ran you down with my bike! I have to go now. The game is afoot!"

"Where are you off to?" Mr. Neederhouse called as Hannah pedaled away.

"108 Shady Lane!" she cried over her shoulder.

CHAPTER 15

WHEN HANNAH ARRIVED at the Lambert's house, she found Lacy in her bedroom, lying on her bed crying.

"I've looked through all the video footage from the drone *three times* in *slow motion* and I couldn't find Mr. Meowgi!" said Lacy.

"I'm very sorry, Lacy," said Hannah, taking a seat on the edge of the bed.

"However, I did find our missing garbage can lid on the side of a road," said Lacy. "But I'd rather have found Mr. Meowgi."

"But, listen, that drone search was a longshot to begin with," said Hannah. "Besides, I've got more good news for you. I think I may have caught a major break in your case. I think I may know who has Mr. Meowgi."

Lacy sat up on her bed. "That's wonderful! Can we go get him?"

"Not just yet," said Hannah. She removed her bubble pipe from her rainbow fanny pack and produced a few bubbles. "First, I need to see your doorbell camera video one more time."

The girls again consulted with Lacy's parents and then went to a computer to find the video files.

"I'm looking for the video of the jogger with the cute lime-green jogging clothes and the ponytail," said Hannah, clicking on the files. "There!"

Hannah and Lacy watched the video. As before, they saw the lady jogger jogging along the sidewalk, her lime-green suit showing pleasantly in the sunshine and her ponytail swinging cutely. But she took only two seconds to pass completely through the video. She was there and gone. And the video quality was not exactly perfect.

"I can't tell if she's wearing a backpack," said Hannah, squinting. She blew more bubbles from the pipe. They seemed frustrated as they floated in the air, popping one by one.

"You can slow down the video and watch it frame-by-frame," said Lacy. "You can zoom in, too. I've learned a lot about searching video footage lately."

Lacy clicked on the video, adjusted the settings, and when the video played again, Hannah could clearly see that the mystery jogger lady was indeed wearing a large backpack.

Hannah's response to this was to blow a bountiful breath into the bubble pipe. The remaining soapy fluid in the pipe was instantly converted to a veritable fleet of surprisingly large bubbles. Just then a breeze blew through the house, and the bubbles were carried out of a window and into the yard, where they apparently caught the very same draft the trash can lid had wafted upon, and the bubbles were transported away in the same direction, into the same neighboring yard.

"The jogger lady *is* wearing a backpack!" cried Hannah. "You can't see it in the full-speed video, but there it is! And your mail carrier, Mr. Neederhouse, was absolutely right—it's a *big* backpack! One that would easily hold Mr. Meowgi!"

Just then, the doorbell rang. Actually, that's not the right way to put it. It would be better to say that Lacy's doorbell began to go *ding-dong-ding-dong-ding-dong-ding*.

"That's odd," said Hannah, turning around in the chair. "That sounds like *my* doorbell-ringing technique."

The two girls hurried to the door, and who did they find but Mia Miller.

"Mia!" cried Hannah and Lacy together.

"I'm so pleased to see you!" confessed Hannah. "But I thought you were studying for your social studies test!"

"Science," said Mia. "I'm finished now, and I have big, *big* news about the Mr. Meowgi case!"

"*You* have big, big news?" asked Hannah, barely able to contain herself. "So do I!"

Several minutes passed as Mia and Hannah tried to determine who would be first to reveal their news.

"You go *first*, Mia," said Hannah in a polite tone.

"No, *you* should go first," replied Mia, her tone even more polite.

"I wouldn't *think* of going first," cooed Hannah, her tone practically dripping in politeness.

"Hannah, don't make me *insist*," purred Mia.

Round and round they went, each pleading with progressively more politeness.

"Hold it!" said Lacy, stepping between the two sleuths at last. "This is getting us nowhere!"

"She's right," said Hannah.

Mia nodded her head.

"It's *my* cat and *my* case," said Lacy. "So, *I'll* decide. Hannah, you go first."

"Thank you for your assistance, Lacy," said Hannah with a slight bow. "Okay. Mia. You'll never believe it. I discovered that the mystery jogger lady in Lacy's doorbell's video footage is wearing a backpack big enough to pack away Mr. Meowgi!"

Mia's eyes grew wide, and she seemed almost a little afraid. "Oh, my goodness," she breathed.

"What?" said Hannah. "What is it?"

"Yeah," echoed Lacy. "What is it?"

Mia blinked and seemed to recover herself somewhat. "The mystery jogger is no mystery. While I was studying my science notes, I remembered why she looks so familiar!"

"Why? Why?" cried Hannah and Mia.

"The mystery jogger lady with the cute ponytail," said Mia, "is none other than Patricia Patagonia, proprietor of Patty's Pet Palace!"

CHAPTER 16

It is a beautiful day to launch another rocket to extinguish the sun, thought Robert the Robot.

He and his re-programmed, re-built robot cohorts had worked nonstop to build an even bigger, badder, and more-destructive rocket. And not only did it look bigger and badder, it was a *better* rocket than the last. This one had an internal guidance system. In other words, it did not have to be aimed at the sun like an arrow aimed at a target. Once this new rocket was launched, it would find its own way to the sun, regardless of whether a silly garbage can lid flew over the fence and knocked it off course by 1.081118 centimeters.

Robert had been able to determine that it was a garbage can lid that had foiled his second plan to blot out the sun. He felt annoyed and humiliated that it had been a garbage can lid of all things. In fact, he almost could not believe it.

It is just so silly! thought Robert. *A spinning trash can lid comes sailing over the fence and ruins such a beautifully scientific and technologically marvelous plan as mine? Absurd. If someone wrote that in a storybook, no one would even believe it!*

The new rocket gleamed in the tranquil sunlight. Robert knew he should have built a rocket like this one to begin with, but he didn't have the circuitry he needed. The circuits and computer programming needed for a rocket with internal guidance takes a very long time to design and create. A rocket with internal guidance is almost like a rocket with its own brain, and Robert just didn't have the time to build that kind of rocket. George would be in Australia for only another three weeks or so. The sun had to be blocked out before that. And so Robert, with his highly advanced neural network, had hit upon an ingenious idea.

He would use part of his *own* brain to give the rocket a brain.

Using the advanced technology found in George's robot fabrication facility, Robert decided that he would carefully detach a small piece of his own neural network and place it into the new rocket.

It was the perfect solution, and he knew that George would be proud of his ingenuity.

George started the neural network detachment in the morning on Wednesday, and by that same afternoon he was ready to transfer the neural circuit to the internal guidance system of the rocket. Then he would set the controls for the heart of the sun and launch the rocket. Next the rocket would steer itself to the sun, set off a massive nuclear chain reaction, and no one (including George) would ever be bothered by sunlight again.

As was mentioned earlier in the story, George Gevol had designed the neural networks of his robots to be contained in super-hard steel cases so that they were almost indestructible. George did this so that if one of his robots were destroyed in an explosion or run over by a steam-roller, the robot's brain would be undamaged and the robot could be rebuilt.

Robert knew he would have to open up the super-hard steel container in his head, where his own neural network was stored, so that he could remove the small neural circuit he needed to program the internal guidance of the sun-killing rocket. This was a delicate operation, and he had to be careful. But Robert was smart and well-trained, and he was successful in removing the neural circuit he needed. Then he quickly closed the super-hard case.

Next, he placed the neural circuit into a padded box and took it out into the backyard, where the new rocket awaited. There was a small door on one side of the rocket, and Robert opened it so that he could install the neural circuit. The rocket would then have its own brain, and it would be able to fly itself to the sun.

You might have already figured out what happened next.

A flotilla of bulbous, soapy bubbles came wafting over the backyard fence. Robert was preoccupied with carefully installing the circuit, so he did not see the bubbles. But Linda Clipper saw them. And so did Heavy D. Having a professional background in soap and bubbles, Suds McGee was particularly impressed.

"Oooh, bubbles," said Suds. "Wow, see how big they are!"

Robert turned around to face them.

"Hush, you robots!" said Robert. "I am in the middle of an exceedingly delicate procedure! There must be no distractions!"

But it was too late. The bubbles were billowing on the breeze directly at Robert.

Several bubbles popped on Robert's nose and face, covering his vision units (his eyes) with a soapy film. This so startled Robert that he dropped the neural network circuit on the launching pad.

"Nooo," cried Robert, his robotic voice sounding very pathetic. He leaned down to pick up the small chip, but his eyes were smeared with soap, and he couldn't find it.

Meanwhile, many of the remaining bubbles popped against the rocket. Some of them popped inside the rocket's brain compartment. This may not seem like a very big problem, because this rocket was designed to fly into the sun itself, a.k.a. Sol, the temperature of which is almost 6,000 degrees Kelvin! However, the circuitry inside the rocket was not protected from soapy water, which is what bubbles are made of. Soapy water does terrible things to electronic circuits, and these bubbles did terrible things to the inside of Robert's new rocket. It buzzed and sparked and hissed alarmingly.

The damage could probably have been repaired by Robert, but he panicked when he heard the hissing and saw the sparking, and he staggered half-blindly toward the rocket in a desperate attempt to save a third project from being spoiled. As he did so, he heard a faint crackling sound under his foot. It was like the sound of someone stepping on a pair of eyeglasses.

Robert had stepped on the neural circuit, the brain of the rocket. His heavy aluminum foot had crushed it into a fine, glassy powder. This upset Robert so much that he bumbled into the launching controls of the new rocket and accidentally hit the *LAUNCH* button.

None of the robots—not Heavy, Linda, nor Suds —could do anything but watch as the rocket, still sparking and smoking, flew off into the beautiful blue sky, spiraled and looped a few times, and then exploded in mid-air.

There was a new wave of U.F.O. reports to the Air Force and police, but when these sightings were investigated, it was concluded that it had been a rather beautiful display of illegal fireworks (the Fourth of July was still many months away).

CHAPTER 17

Hannah and Mia jumped on their bikes and propelled themselves to Patty's Pet Palace in downtown Cardwick. They arrived just before closing time. As they parked their bikes, they saw Patricia Patagonia, the mystery jogger lady with the cute ponytail and lime-green jogging suit, inside the store.

A little bell jingled above the door as Hannah and Mia sauntered into the pet shop. They went directly to the pet cages, where kittens and cats were kept, but Mr. Meowgi wasn't there.

"Hi, kids," said Ms. Patagonia in a friendly voice. She was standing behind a glass-enclosed counter, totaling up her receipts for the day. Her ponytail swung merrily as she turned to Mia and Hannah. "Do you need any help? Needing a new pet? I've got some lovely new turtles. Oh, and I have a selection of chinchillas."

Hannah was wearing her oversized sunglasses, which glinted in the light of the late afternoon sun. Her bubble pipe had been refilled and was clamped at a confident angle between her teeth. She approached Ms. Patagonia's counter.

"No," said Hannah, peering precociously over her big shades, "we're *not* looking for pets. We're just *looking*."

"Oh, okay," said Ms. Patagonia. "Well, how can I help you?"

"I'll ask the questions, if you don't mind," said Hannah in an arrogant and even impolite tone. "You see, my name is Hannah, and I am Cardwick's leading kid detective and private investigator. In case you're wondering, my name is spelled the same both ways, frontward and back. This is my partner, Mia."

"I see," said Ms. Patagonia, now looking quite perplexed. "Well, Hannah and Mia, I'm Patricia Patagonia, and I'm the proprietor of Patty's Pet—"

"Yes, yes," said Hannah with a dismissive wave of her hand. "We know who you are, Ms. Patagonia. And we know what you've been up to."

"I'm not sure I understand," said Ms. Patagonia, raising one eyebrow.

Mia came up behind Hannah and whispered, "Hannah, take it easy! Don't be rude!"

Hannah leaned against the counter, so that her back was to Ms. Patagonia. She winked at Mia. "All right," drawled Hannah. "I'll come right to the point." Hannah spun around quickly to face Ms. Patagonia and yelled, *"Tell us what brand of canned tuna fish you prefer!"*

Ms. Patagonia recoiled as though someone had thrown a cold glass of water in her face. "Well, first of all," she said to Hannah, "I'm not sure I appreciate your tone. You're not being very polite."

"Toldja," hissed Mia out of the side of her mouth.

Hannah thought about this.

"Secondly," Ms. Patagonia continued, "I don't prefer *any* brand of canned tuna fish because I don't eat canned tuna fish."

"All right," said Hannah, continuing even though she now sounded somewhat unsure, "then why don't you tell us why you were wearing a great big backpack when you jogged past 108 Shady Lane last Tuesday and Wednesday!"

Ms. Patagonia again recoiled, surprised and confused at this bizarre line of questioning.

"All right, Hannah," she said. "I'll answer your

question. But then you're going to do two things for *me*. You're going to apologize for your rude—and, might I add, bizarre—behavior. And then you're going to tell me what this is all about."

Hannah had been trying to act like a real hard-boiled detective. She'd been trying to act like the private eye with a tough exterior and all the answers. But Ms. Patagonia was right—she *was* being impolite, and it wasn't helping the case. Hannah swallowed hard and blinked behind her big sunglasses.

Mia was still standing quietly behind Hannah. "I think Ms. Patagonia has a point, Hannah," she said. "So, let's listen to what she has to say and then we'll do as she has asked."

"Thank you, Mia," said Ms. Patagonia. "Now then. You are correct. I *was* wearing a backpack last week on Shady Lane. It's right here." She bent down, grabbed a large backpack from the floor, and held it up for Mia and Hannah to see. Then she went on. "In case you didn't notice my sign out front, I offer free delivery of any items that will fit into this backpack, to anywhere in Cardwick, during my afternoon run. I deliver cat food, dog chews, reptile hot rocks, fish flakes—anything that will fit in my pack. This way, I get exercise and also help people who don't drive or who are at work when my shop is open."

Hannah stood still for a moment, then said, "I see. Well. That certainly sheds a lot of light on the matter."

"Okay, Hannah," said Mia, standing behind her, "now it's your turn."

Ms. Patagonia stood behind her counter with her arms folded.

"Ms. Patagonia," Hannah began with a sigh.

"You may call me Patricia," said Patricia.

"Oh, okay," stammered Hannah with a nervous nod. "Well, I'm awfully sorry, Patricia, for hassling you and for being impolite. It's just that Mia and I are on a difficult case to find a missing cat, and I think I may have misinterpreted some of the clues." She produced her evidence notebook and flipped through the pages at random. "I sometimes get a little out of control when I'm working a case, you see, and, well, I apologize."

Patricia nodded sympathetically and said, "A missing cat, you say? And I'm a suspect because I own a pet shop?"

"Something like that," said Hannah. "As I mentioned, I have a tendency to throw myself into my work, and I might get a little carried away sometimes."

"I understand," said Patricia. "I'm the same way

sometimes, and there's really no harm done, so maybe I can help you on your missing cat case."

"That would be great," said Mia.

Hannah rummaged in the rainbow fanny pack and produced the photos of Mr. Meowgi. She laid them on the counter for Patricia to see.

"Hey," said Patricia, "isn't this Mr. Meowgi? The Lambert's cat?"

"Yes!" said Hannah. "You know him?"

"I know most of the cats and dogs in this town," said Patricia. "Mr. Meowgi is a wonderful old Corellian Couch Cat. The Lamberts buy kibble and ear medicine here at my shop. I hadn't heard that he was missing. Why didn't they come tell me, or bring some flyers, or post some pictures on Facelook?"

"If we ever work another missing cat case," said Mia, "that's the first thing we'll do. But we're convinced that Mr. Meowgi was abducted."

"Why do you say that?" asked Patricia.

Mia looked at Hannah, waiting for her to tell Patricia all about the case. But Hannah was standing still now, staring into space, as if she'd just received shocking news.

And so Mia stepped up and said, "For one thing, we found a can of half-eaten tuna fish in the Lambert's garbage can, and it's a different brand than the one they buy. That made us think that someone lured Mr. Meowgi outside with the tuna, and then grabbed him."

Patricia nodded.

"And there's another clue," said Mia. "Mr. Meowgi's collar was found outside, unbuckled, as though the catnapper removed it so that no one could identify him."

Patricia nodded again.

"Also," Mia went on, "Mr. Meowgi is a big and fat and lazy inside-cat, not to mention somewhat old, and so it just doesn't seem possible that he suddenly got out of the house and ran away."

"This is pretty good detective work," said Patricia. "I agree with all of your conclusions. So, what's next? Do you have any other suspects—besides me?"

Mia looked at Hannah again, but she was still just staring and blinking, her mouth open slightly.

"Hannah?" said Mia, giving Hannah a nudge with her elbow. "Hannah, what are we going to do next?"

Hannah blinked a few more times and then shook her head, as if she were coming out of a trance. Then she looked at Patricia and said, "Patricia, did you say Mr. Meowgi is a *Corellian Couch Cat?*"

"Yes," replied Patricia, "and a fine specimen at that. You might think he's a little, well—"

"—ugly?" said Hannah.

Patricia chuckled and said, "I was going to say 'odd-looking,' but yes, you might think Mr. Meowgi is, um, not beautiful, but he looks exactly the way a Corellian Couch Cat should look. Corellian Couch Cats are also quite rare. I've asked the Lamberts why they don't take Mr. Meowgi to cat shows. He'd surely win a prize. There's a cat show next weekend."

"A cat show?" stuttered Hannah.

"Yeah, it's just down the road in Baskerville," said Patricia. "Why?"

Hannah slapped a hand to her forehead. "Gad-zooks!" she cried. "Now I *really* know who took Mr. Meowgi!"

CHAPTER 18

Patricia had to close up her shop, so she couldn't help the two sleuths any more that day, but Hannah and Mia assured her that they'd stay in touch, and then they ran out of the pet store to return to Mrs. Beechtree's cottage. When they arrived, they set their bikes in the grass and then climbed the steps of the front porch.

"I've got her!" said Hannah, preparing to knock on the door. "Mia, I've got her! All I have to do is go in there and prove it!"

"Whoa there, Nellie," said Mia. She took hold of Hannah's arm to stop her from knocking. "Take a breath. We can't storm in there and act rude and accuse Mrs. Beechtree. It'll upset her too much."

"But she stole Mr. Meowgi!" cried Hannah, raising her fist again to knock. "She's a catnapper!"

"You don't know that for sure," said Mia. She lowered Hannah's arm again.

"I'm almost one hundred percent sure, Mia! We gotta go in there and bust this case wide open!"

"I'm sorry, Hannah, but we can't," said Mia.

If the two sleuths had been paying closer attention, they'd have noticed a tall and mysterious figure on the sidewalk in front of Mrs. Beechtree's house. His hat was pulled down over his eyes, and he wore a long coat with the collar flipped up to hide his face. It would have been difficult for Hannah or Mia to recognize him, but they didn't notice him at all. They didn't notice that he seemed to slow down as he passed them by, like he was listening to what they were saying. Soon the mysterious figure continued down the sidewalk and out of view.

"If you think Mrs. Beechtree is guilty," Mia was saying, "we'll ask her our sleuthing questions, but we have to keep our minds open, be respectful, and remember that we all live together in the same community. We're kinda like a big family. You're taking things too far, you're taking things to extremes, and you've lost sight of what you set out to do in the first place—to save the world right here in Cardwick."

Hannah turned and sat down heavily on Mrs. Beechtree's front steps. Mia joined her.

"Gadzooks," Hannah breathed. "You're right again, Mia. I'm so glad you finished studying for that trigonometry test."

"Science," said Mia.

"Right," said Hannah. "Anyway, I nearly spoiled everything with my hard-boiled private eye act."

"Glad to help," said Mia. "Now, should we go and talk to Mrs. Beechtree?"

"Yes," said Hannah. "Let's go."

Hannah and Mia stood up and knocked on the door. Mrs. Beechtree answered the door and invited them inside.

After they'd gone in, however, the mysterious figure returned to the sidewalk in front of Mrs. Beechtree's house, as though he were looking for the two girls.

CHAPTER 19

Mrs. Beechtree wasn't quite as happy to see Hannah this time, nor did she seem thrilled to see Mia. She tried to *act* as though she were glad to have company again, but both of the sleuths noticed she was nervous.

"Come in," Mrs. Beechtree said flatly. "Come in and sit down."

Mia and Hannah went in and sat in the parlor on the overstuffed chairs. Mrs. Beechtree sat on the sofa.

"What can I do for you this time?" said Mrs. Beechtree to Hannah. "And who's this with you?"

"This is Mia," said Hannah. "She and I do detective work together. She was studying for a history exam when I visited earlier."

"Science," Mia said.

"I see," said Mrs. Beechtree quietly. "Yes, well,

would you like some more cookies? I—I have oat-chip, peanut-meal, or chocolate-butter."

"Mrs. Beechtree," said Hannah, "I'm actually super hungry from running around town looking for Mr. Meowgi. Could I trouble you for a sandwich?"

Mrs. Beechtree swallowed and knitted her brows. "A sandwich? Well, I—I suppose. What kind of sandwich would you like?"

"Tuna fish, please," said Hannah. Her eyes darted to Mia.

Mia gave a small nod.

"Oh, tuna fish, sure," said Mrs. Beechtree, and then turning to Mia she said, "Can I get anything for you, my dear?"

"No, thank you," said Mia.

"Well, then," said Mrs. Beechtree, rising from the sofa, "you two wait here. I won't be a minute."

Hannah waited until Mrs. Beechtree had left the room, and then she picked up the picture frame she'd noticed on her first visit, the one that had been set face-down. Hannah looked at the picture in the frame. It was just as she'd thought. She showed it to Mia, who nodded. Hannah tucked the framed photo under her arm, and she and Mia then stood and went into Mrs. Beechtree's kitchen.

"We thought you might like some help," said Hannah.

"Oh, that won't be necessary," said Mrs. Beechtree. Beads of sweat stood out on her forehead, even though it was quite cool in the kitchen. She chuckled nervously. "I won't be a—a minute."

Mrs. Beechtree was preparing the tuna fish salad. The empty can sat nearby on the kitchen counter. It was the brand with the label that showed a little blue cartoon fish wearing glasses. Hannah and Mia saw the can and nodded to one another.

"Mrs. Beechtree," said Hannah. "I'm awfully sorry that Pablo Picatso ran away from home, but taking someone else's cat is wrong."

Hannah held up the picture in the frame from the parlor so that Mrs. Beechtree could see it. It was a photo of Pablo Picatso, of course, with a big blue ribbon that read *BEST IN SHOW*. Pablo looked almost exactly like Mr. Meowgi, except Mr. Meowgi had white on his chin and Pablo didn't. Mrs. Beechtree looked at the photo and then paused her sandwich-making.

Hannah said, "We know you lured Mr. Meowgi away with a can of that tuna fish after you dropped off cookies at the Lamberts last Wednesday. We know you're planning to take him to Baskerville for the cat show."

Then Mia spoke. "The Lamberts are heartbroken and worried sick about Mr. Meowgi. He's okay, isn't he?"

"Oh, yes," said Mrs. Beechtree. Tears were gathering in her eyes. "He's quite well. He's unharmed, well fed, and safe."

"That's great," said Hannah softly.

"He's just such a wonderful cat," said Mrs. Beechtree, sniffling back her tears. "And he reminds me so much of my poor Pablo! I miss him so much!"

"We understand," said Mia.

All at once Mrs. Beechtree stood up straight and said, "Please wait here. I won't be a minute."

Then she left the kitchen. Mia and Hannah traded a nervous glance, but Mrs. Beechtree reappeared in less than a minute, and in her arms, she carried Mr. Meowgi. Mrs. Beechtree seemed to struggle under the weight of the burden. She labored into the kitchen and she set the cat down on the counter with a great sigh of relief.

It was the first time either Hannah or Mia had seen Mr. Meowgi in person. The photographs supplied by Lacy simply did not do him justice. Mr. Meowgi was truly enormous, bigger than many of the neighborhood dogs and indeed larger than a few of the neighborhood children. The cat's misshapen head was nearly the size of a football, and his swollen belly rested heavily on the counter like an overfilled water balloon covered in fur. Mr. Meowgi's ears swiveled around continuously like a feline radar station, and his dirty-yellow eyes were half-shut, giving his puggish face a peevish expression. He gazed around the kitchen as if he owned the place but wasn't very happy about that. And he might have been looking at Hannah and Mrs. Beechtree, or maybe he was watching Mia and the open can of tuna fish—the way the eyes always pointed in two different directions made it hard to tell.

Hannah and Mia stared at him with unconcealed amazement.

"Gadzooks," whispered Hannah.

We will not refer to Mr. Meowgi as "ugly." We might say his appearance was "unusual," "striking," or even "alarming." Mr. Meowgi was definitely unlike a typical cat. However, it was obvious he'd been lovingly cared for. His brown and orange fur looked tangled and mussed, but on closer inspection it was clean and had been recently brushed. Also, despite his disgruntled expression, Mr. Meowgi was *purring.*

"Isn't he magnificent?" breathed Mrs. Beechtree. "I was going to return him, you know. Really. I only wanted to take him to the cat show in Baskerville. Like old times with Pablo. Then I was going to drop him off anonymously at the Lambert's house."

Mrs. Beechtree stroked Mr. Meowgi's back, and the cat's crazy eyes closed contentedly. Hannah reached out cautiously to scratch Mr. Meowgi's massive head, and Mia patted his ponderous belly. The purring grew louder. It sounded like a lawnmower beneath a pile of blankets.

Mrs. Beechtree removed her spectacles and wiped her eyes with her apron. Then she sighed heavily. "I want to thank you for coming, Mia and Hannah. I've made a terrible mistake. Do you think I can ever make it right again? Do you think the Lambert family will ever forgive me?"

"Why don't we all go over to their house and find out," said Mia.

CHAPTER 20

Robert the Robot was feeling very low.

No matter how he'd tried to carry out the parting wishes of his friend and inventor, George, Robert had been foiled and frustrated. At first, he'd been very excited about his various sun-blocking plans, but they didn't feel right anymore. Robert felt there was something off or wrong about what he was doing, but he couldn't figure out what it was.

And Robert had another feeling, too. He felt tired. You know that robots don't require sleep and, in fact, as long as their batteries are charged, they don't even need to sit down to rest. But Robert felt tired in another way—he wanted to do something different. He wanted to read books, watch movies, and go for walks. He didn't *need* to rest, but he sure *wanted* to.

It's funny that Robert had no idea that this was what George also wanted him to do. That morning earlier in the month, when George was leaving for Australia, he'd meant to tell Robert to rest and relax —he'd just forgotten to in all the confusion.

Robert had seen George leave the house many times to take walks. If George were frustrated, for example, he'd go on a walk and come back in a more pleasant state of mind. If George were puzzling over a problem, he'd go for a walk to think about it. George even went on walks when he was feeling good, and this seemed to make him feel even better.

I am going for a walk, thought Robert. *I shall go for a walk and see if it makes me feel better.*

Robert the Robot probably could have walked around Cardwick without attracting too much attention. Robots were becoming more common everywhere. And besides, a lot of people in Cardwick walked around with their eyes on the sky, looking for U.F.O.s. Nevertheless, Robert put on one of George's hats and a long coat, and then he went out.

This turned out to be a great idea. As Robert strolled down the sidewalk of Shady Lane, he began to feel better immediately. He let his mind wander, he let the worries of his project fall away, and he listened to the sounds of Cardwick. Birds were chirping. Kids were laughing. Sprinklers on the lawns were going *ch-ch-ch-ch-ch-ch-ch!* The blue sky was dotted with downy, cottony clouds, and a mild breeze carried the aroma of blooming flowers.

Robert approached the house where a nice lady lived who often brought fresh-baked cookies to George. As Robert passed by the house, he heard two children speaking with one another, and he couldn't help himself from listening in. Robert's hearing was much more acute than that of any human, so he was able to hear the whole conversation. This is the part of the conversation Robert found most interesting:

"Remember that we all live together in the same community. We're kinda like a big family. You're taking things too far, you're taking things to extremes, and you've lost sight of what you set out to do in the first place—to save the world right here in Cardwick."

Robert didn't know what the two children were speaking about, but his thinking changed as soon as he heard this. Because Robert himself had been going to extremes, and he'd lost sight of what he needed to do.

His neural network suddenly understood that he'd made a big mistake, and he had completely misunderstood George's instructions and intentions.

George doesn't want me to block out the sun, thought Robert. *He only wanted me to shade the sun so he could write something down. It would have been a terrible catastrophe to shoot a rocket at the sun!*

Robert turned around and returned to the house where he'd heard the children speaking. He wanted to thank them for helping him learn something really important. However, by then the two kids had apparently gone inside to visit the nice lady who baked cookies. And so Robert walked a different direction and had a pleasant stroll. He saw ducks quarreling in the city pond. He saw families riding their bikes. Finally, he sat on a bench in the park and did absolutely nothing.

And it felt great!

Later on, Robert returned to his house and informed the other robots that all plans to block out the sun were cancelled, and that because there was not much else to do before George came back, they should go back to their normal duties of washing windows, mowing the lawn, and so forth.

"And when you've finished your chores," announced Robert, "you should relax and rest."

"But we are robots," said Heavy D. "We do not require rest and relaxation."

"I used to think that, too," said Robert. "But now I think everyone needs relaxation."

For his part, Robert unblocked all the windows. He took down the blankets and plywood and cardboard. He gathered up the wreckage of the fallen parasol tower, and he dismantled the rocket launching pad, and he threw it all onto the scrap heap out in the backyard.

After that, he tidied up the house a bit, watered the plants, sat down on the couch, and read a long book on the history of the universe. Being a robot, Robert needed only 22.5 minutes to finish it. So, he put his feet on the coffee table and read a few more books. In the evening, he went to see a movie about superheroes fighting super-criminals. On his way back, he stopped at Kramer's Grocery Store for a frozen pizza. He cooked the pizza at home, watched a little TV, and then he plugged himself in to recharge his batteries.

The next day, Robert did pretty much the same thing. He realized that he was on vacation, just as George was. And so he was sure to do his chores and keep the house tidy, but he relaxed a lot, too. This went on for two more weeks, and Robert enjoyed himself immensely.

Then an interesting thing happened. Robert

became so relaxed, he felt ready to get back to work. He missed his friend George, and he looked forward to George's return, so that they could collaborate on research projects and experiments again.

All at once, Robert realized that the day had come for George's return. It was almost like time had passed by faster than usual, and he remembered that the same thing had happened to George.

"Hello, Robert!" cried George as he burst through the front door.

"Hello, George," replied Robert.

George gave Robert a big hug. This felt a bit like hugging a filing cabinet, but George didn't mind.

"So, what have you been doing all month?" asked George.

"Well," replied Robert, "you might say I helped to save the world."

"What?" said George, his eyes growing wide. "Was there a disaster? Are you all right? What happened? Was it serious?"

And then another interesting thing happened. Robert laughed. "No," said Robert, with a hint of irony in his robotic voice. "I'm only kidding." And then he said, "Ha. Ha. Ha."

This wasn't a very funny joke, and George didn't really even *get it*. Nevertheless, he laughed and laughed, pleased that his robot pal was developing a sense of humor.

"So," said George, "what did you really do?"

"Nothing, really," said the robot. "Just sat around the house, relaxing and enjoying myself."

George smiled and said, "That's just what I was hoping you'd say."

CHAPTER 21

Both Hannah and Mia thought the Baskerville Regional Cat Show was really something to see.

The Lamberts had decided that Mr. Meowgi might like going to cat shows, and they decided that the show in Baskerville would be Mr. Meowgi's first. Not surprisingly, they invited Hannah and Mia to come along. However, it may come as a surprise to you that they'd also decided that Mrs. Beechtree should be Mr. Meowgi's cat show coach. She told the Lambert family what to expect at cat shows, and she helped Mr. Meowgi prepare to participate.

When Mrs. Beechtree returned Mr. Meowgi to the Lambert family, Lacy and the rest of her family had been quite upset. They were very unhappy with Mrs. Beechtree. However, after thinking it over, they realized that Mr. Meowgi had only been gone for one week, and he was definitely unharmed. In fact, he seemed to be in a slightly better mood after his catnapping. What Mrs. Beechtree had done was wrong, but the Lamberts decided to forgive her and not press charges for catnapping. They even invited Mrs. Beechtree to visit Mr. Meowgi on a regular basis, and it was she who suggested that the big strange kitty be registered for cat shows.

The cat show was held in a large building in downtown Baskerville. Hannah and Mia were amazed at the variety of cats. There were big cats and small cats. There were cats with long white flowing fur, cats with short shiny black fur, and cats with no fur at all. Hannah and Mia saw American Long Hair Cats and American Wire Hair Cats. They saw Bombay Cats, Burmese Cats, and British Short Hair Cats. When the cats were not participating in the show, they stayed in small wire hutches so that people could see them.

They watched cats run through obstacle courses and parade proudly for spectators. In each event, the cats were evaluated by judges, who gave them various scores and awarded prizes.

When it was time for Mr. Meowgi to be shown, Hannah, Mia, and the Lambert family took their seats to watch. Patricia Patagonia was there, too. Mrs.

Beechtree brought Mr. Meowgi into a room and set him on a pedestal. As she did so, there came a chorus of "ooo"s and "aaah"s from the audience, and the judges conferred excitedly among themselves. Mia and Hannah looked around, slightly perplexed at this reaction, and then they looked at one another and shrugged.

"Isn't he extraordinary?" whispered Patricia to Mia and Hannah.

"That's one way of putting it," said Hannah. "Everyone seems to be really impressed with him."

Mia said, "I told you that beauty is in the eye of the beholder."

Mr. Meowgi sat and simply stared, always in two different directions, of course, but seemingly without much interest in what was going on around him. However, Mia and Hannah had gotten to know Mr. Meowgi in the previous couple weeks, and they knew that, even though he didn't show it, he was enjoying the attention.

"Look at Mr. Meowgi," whispered Mia. "He's really loving this!"

"Yeah," whispered Hannah, "it's written all over his face!"

Patricia grinned and nodded.

The judges spent a long time examining Mr.

Meowgi's hair, tail, whiskers, and eyes. They measured him and weighed him and nodded and made notes. Then they spoke to each other again and nodded some more. Mr. Meowgi hadn't scored very high in the events where cats had to run fast or jump high, or do tricks, but he seemed to be doing extremely well at sitting still and, well, just being Mr. Meowgi.

Many other cats were brought before the judges. They were all graceful and beautiful in their own way. However, whenever Mrs. Beechtree placed Mr. Meowgi back in his hutch, there was always a crowd of admirers around him.

Near the end of the cat show, everyone got ready for the *BEST IN SHOW* award to be announced. This award was given to the cat that was the most remarkable of the entire show, no matter what variety or type of cat.

All the contenders were placed on a long runway, and the judges went from cat to cat, looking, staring, scratching their heads, pointing, and making notes. Then they huddled together for one final conference

Hannah, Mia, Patricia, and everyone else were all on the edges of their seats as they waited for the judges' decision, but none were as nervous as Mrs.

Beechtree. You can probably guess which cat won best in show, but for Hannah and the others, the suspense was almost unbearable.

At last, the lead judge approached the microphone.

"Ladies and gentlemen," said the judge, a tall lady with large, fashionable glasses, "It is my pleasure and honor to announce the prize for Best in Show at the Baskerville Regional Cat Show. This year's winner is a newcomer that we hope we'll be seeing a lot more of. My best in show is the Corellian Couch Cat, Mr. Meowgi!"

The audience rose to their feet, applauding and cheering wildly. Even people whose cats did not win awards clapped and cheered for Mr. Meowgi. He was a universal favorite. The judge would have liked to lift Mr. Meowgi high into the air for everyone to see, but this was simply not possible. The best she could do was heave the massive cat up a couple feet in the air like a sack of potatoes. Mr. Meowgi blinked calmly as he sagged down from the judge's trembling arms.

Lacy and the Lamberts were very proud, of course, but they let Mrs. Beechtree accept the gigantic, frilly blue ribbon. She had a tear in her eye as the judge handed the ribbon to her, and she attached the ribbon to Mr. Meowgi's collar.

That evening, when the cat show had ended, Hannah and Mia went out to the parking lot, where they waited for the Lamberts and Mrs. Beechtree to collect Mr. Meowgi.

"Well, Hannah," said Mia. "Another case brought to a successful conclusion."

"I never could have done it without you, Mia," replied Hannah. "I tried—I tried it on my own while you were studying for your literacy class."

"Science," corrected Mia.

"Right," said Hannah. "I tried working on the case alone, but it was a disaster. I misinterpreted the clues and I behaved impolitely to Patricia Patagonia of Patty's Pet Palace. Oh, and I almost ran over a U.S. postal worker! I don't ever want to go solo again!"

"I'll do whatever I can, partner," said Mia.

"Thanks, partner," said Hannah.

"So, what are we going to do tomorrow?" asked Mia.

Hannah put a finger to her chin and thought about this. "Well," she said, "I have a theory about why Mr. Norris's pink flamingos keep disappearing from his flower bed, and I want to investigate."

"Hmm," said Mia. "Well, *I'd* like to take a bike ride to the top of Cherry Tree Peak and have a picnic."

"How about *this*," said Hannah. "I've heard reports of mysterious goings-on at the Cardwick Cemetery. We could bring some flashlights and stay out late to check it out."

"*Or* we could have a sleepover at my house," said Mia. "We could make a big bowl of popcorn, and watch old detective movies."

The two friends kept at it, trading suggestions and debating all the way back to Cardwick. They still hadn't decided what they wanted to do when the Lamberts dropped them off at their homes, and they'd still be undecided the next day.

However, one thing seemed sure: if there were ever anymore trouble in Cardwick, Hannah and Mia would always be ready to save the world.

THANK you for joining me in the story of how Hannah and Mia saved the world. I hope you had as much fun reading the book as I had writing it.

If you have a few moments, it would mean the world to me if you would leave an honest review about the book on the retail site of your choice. Your help in spreading the word is greatly appreciated. Reviews from readers help make a huge difference in assisting new readers in finding books they'll enjoy.

May you keep reading and saving the world in your own way wherever you happen to be.

Love, A.M. Luzzader

P.S. If you'd like to know when my next book is out and also receive occasional updates on bonus offers, freebies, and special deals, please sign up for my newsletter at www.amluzzader.com.

A.M. Luzzader is an award-winning children's author who writes chapter books and middle grade books. She specializes in writing books for preteens. A.M.'s fantasy adventure series 'A Mermaid in Middle Grade' is a magical coming of age book for ages 8-12. She is also the author of the 'Hannah Saves the World' series, which is a children's mystery adventure, also for ages 8-12.

A.M. decided she wanted to write fun stories for

kids when she was still a kid herself. By the time she was in fourth grade, she was already writing short stories. In fifth grade, she bought a typewriter at a garage sale to put her words into print, and in sixth grade she added illustrations. Now that she has decided what she wants to be when she grows up, A.M. writes books for girls and boys full time. She was selected as the Writer of the Year in 2019-2020 by the League of Utah Writers.

A.M. is the mother of a 10-year-old and a 13-year-old who often inspire her stories. She lives with her husband and children in northern Utah. She is a devout cat person and avid reader.

A.M. Luzzader's books are appropriate for ages 5-12. Her chapter books are intended for kindergarten to third grade, and her middle grade books are for third grade through sixth grade. Find out more about A.M., sign up to receive her newsletter, and get special offers at her website: www.amluzzader.com.

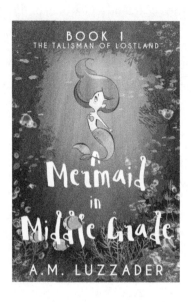

A Mermaid in Middle Grade: Book 1: The Talisman of Lostland

(Available now)

A young mermaid. A sea witch out for revenge. Can Brynn Finley become a sea guardian and help humans in danger when she just barely started the sixth grade?

Brynn Finley is the only mermaid in class who hasn't been able to learn mer-magic. Without it, she can't be a guardian of the sea with her parents and friends. On her quest for answers, Brynn encounters a loveable sea turtle, a pair of selkie sisters, and Phaedra, the great and terrible sea witch. Soon Brynn is over her head in trouble, and she must learn to ask for help if she's going to follow the merfolk oath to be a protector of the ocean and a guardian of the sea.

The Mermaid in Middle Grade series is a middle-grade fantasy adventure series and coming of age books appropriate for ages 8-12 and all who enjoy middle grade books.

Educational topics: Ocean and marine life, environmental conservation, honesty, friendship, mindfulness, bullying, middle school, and interpersonal skills.

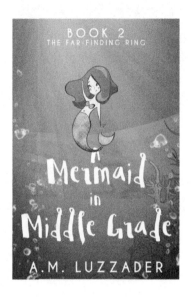

A Mermaid in Middle Grade: Book 2: The Far-Finding Ring

(Available now)

A young mermaid. False accusations. The dreadful sea witch. Can Brynn Finley navigate stormy waters to win back her best friend?

Jade Sands has been Brynn Finley's best friend since they were wee mer-babies. But when Jade's mother thinks Brynn has stolen her cherished pearls, she forbids the two mermaids to see one another. Determined to get her best friend back, Brynn sets out to find Phaedra the sea witch and solve the mystery of the missing jewelry. On her quest, Brynn makes new friends, learns new mer-magic, and discovers what it really means to be a friend.

Educational topics: Ocean and marine life, environmental conservation, bullying, friendship, mindfulness, and interpersonal skills.

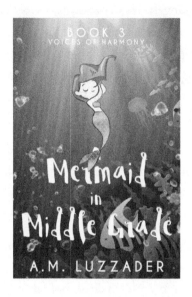

A Mermaid in Middle Grade: Book 3: Voices of Harmony

(Available now)

An unhealthy coral reef and pollution in the ocean. An entire undersea town turned upside-down. Can Brynn Finley solve Fulgent's latest mystery and get to the Jay Barracuda and the Killer Whales concert before Phaedra the sea witch turns her into a lowly sea slug?

When a beautiful and talented young mermaid named Priscilla Banks moves to Fulgent, everything starts going wrong for mermaid Brynn Finley. Her best friend ignores her, the sea witch is set free, and the seafolk of Fulgent are acting very strangely. As Brynn searches for clues, she learns a lot about friendship and settling differences, but time is running out—the sea witch has another dastardly and disgusting scheme to rid the oceans of humans. Soon the entire town is chasing Brynn, and her only friend is her trusty pet sea turtle!

The Mermaid in Middle Grade series is a middle-school fantasy adventure series of coming of age books appropriate for children ages 8–12 and all who enjoy middle grade books.

Educational topics: Ocean and marine life, environmental conservation, mindfulness, envy and jealousy, friendship problems, bullying, middle school, and interpersonal skills.

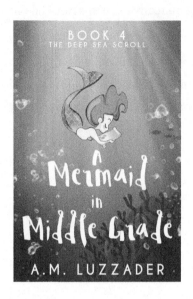

A Mermaid in Middle Grade: Book 4: The Deep Sea Scroll (Available now)

The sea witch is up to mischief again, but Brynn is so busy she feels like she is chasing her own tail. Can she juggle all her responsibilities without falling behind?

Brynn Finley is the star of the Starfish Steppers, the grooviest mer-dance squad in the sea. Brynn is excited for a new dance season and a chance to blow the competition out of the water, but this year it's tougher than she thought. And there's another problem--Brynn's grades at school are slipping. She has too much to do and too little time. As Brynn races wearily from school to rehearsal and back home again, she comes up with a plan to catch up--a very bad plan. Will Brynn really team up with Phaedra the sea witch or will she learn her lesson?

Educational topics: Ocean and marine life, environmental conservation, mindfulness, envy and competition, commitment and responsibility, and the importance of education.

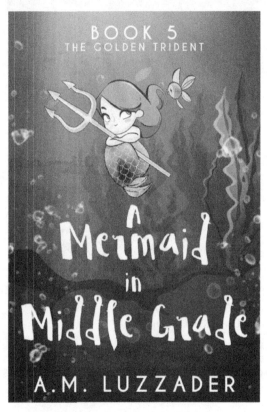

Mermaid in Middle Grade: Book 5: The
Golden Trident

A Mermaid in Middle Grade: Book 6:
The Great Old One

Also, keep an eye out for Hannah Saves the World #3, releasing in 2021!

Made in the USA
Las Vegas, NV
20 November 2023

81168642R00100